BTEC

ALGEBRA III

ANTHONY NICOLAIDES

B.Sc (Eng.) C. Eng. M.I.E.E.
Senior Lecturer and Course Tutor
for the BTEC NATIONAL DIPLOMA IN ENGINEERING

at

LEWISHAM COLLEGE

P.A.S.S. PUBLICATIONS

PRIVATE ACADEMIC & SCIENTIFIC STUDIES LIMITED

©   A. Nicolaides 1991

First Published in Great Britain 1991 by

Private Academic & Scientific Studies Limited.

ISBN 1 872684 13 0

Other titles pulished by the same author in the BTEC series.

Mathematics II
Analytical Mathematics II
Electrical and Electronic Principles II
Calculus III

Other titles published by the same author in the GCE A series.

Complex Numbers
Trigonmetry
Algebra
Cartesian and Polar Curve Sketching
Differential Calculus and Applications.

Printed by Hartnolls Limited
A member of Martins Printing Group
Victoria Square, Bodmin, Cornwall, PL31 IEG

PREFACE

This book, which is part of the BTEC series in Mathematics for technicians, covers thoroughly the topic of ALGEBRA III.

The ALGEBRA III book, like all the books in the series, is divided into two parts. PART I, the theory of ALGEBRA III which consists of ten chapters is extensively dealt with, together with many worked examples and exercises. A step by step approach is adopted throughout.

PART II of this book acts as a problem solver for all the exercises set at the end of each chapter. Topics essential to answering ALGEBRA III exercises are also given special attention.

I am grateful to Sandra Francis for typesetting this book.

The author acknowledges gratefully his indebtedness to BTEC for allowing the syllabus to be published.

A Nicolaides

CONTENTS

1. EXPONENTIAL FUNCTIONS AND NATURAL LOGARITHMS

Evaluates expressions involving exponentials and natural logarithms.

a. Defines natural (Naperian) logarithms.

b. Determines natural (Naperian) logarithms from tables and by calculator.

c. States the relationship between common and natural (Naperian) logarithms.

d. Uses natural (Naperian) logarithms to evaluate expressions arising in technological units.

e. Solves equations involving e^x and $\ln x$.

2. COMPLEX NUMBERS

Extends the number system to complex numbers

a. Defines a complex number.

b. Plots complex numbers on an Argand diagram.

c. Determines the sum and difference of two complex numbers in the form $a + jb$ and relates the results to an Argand diagram.

d. Determines the product of two complex numbers in the form $a + jb$.

e. Defines the conjugate of a complex number.

f. Uses 2e and evaluates $\dfrac{Z_1}{Z_2}$.

3. MODULUS AND ARGUMENT OF COMPLEX NUMBERS

Understands the modulus, argument form of complex numbers.

a.   Converts $a + jb$ into polar form and vice versa.

b.   Defines the modulus and argument of a complex number.

c.   Multiplies and divides complex numbers using the polar form.

d.   Determines the square roots of a complex number.

APPLICATIONS OF COMPLEX NUMBERS IN A.C. THEORY

4. POLAR CO-ORDINATES SIMPLE CURVE SKETCHING

Understands polar coordinates.

a.   Defines polar coordinates, r and Θ.

b.   States the relationships between polar and cartesian coordinates.

c.   Converts cartesian to polar coordinates and vice versa.

d.   Plots graphs of functions defined in polar coordinates such as $r = a, \Theta = \alpha, r = k\Theta, r = 2a$ $r = \cos \Theta$.

5. MATRICES AND DETERMINANTS

Understands the notation of matrices and determinants.

a.   Recognises the notation for a matrix.

b.   Calculates the sum and difference of two matrices (2 x 2 only).

c.   Calculates the product of two matrices (2 x 2 only).

d.   Demonstrates that the product of two matrices is, in general, non-commutative.

e.   Defines the unit matrix.

f.   Recognises the notation for a determinant.

g.   Evaluates a 2 x 2 determinant.

6.   SOLUTIONS OF SIMULTANEOUS EQUATIONS

Solves simultaneous equations with two unknowns using matrices and determinants.

a.   Solves simultaneous linear equations with two unknowns using determinants.

b.   Describes the meaning of a determinant whose value is zero, and defines a singular matrix.

c.   Obtains the inverse of a 2 x 2 matrix.

d.   Solves simultaneous linear equations with two unknowns by means of matrices.

e.   Relates the use of matrices to simple technical problems.

7.   BINOMIAL THEOREM

Understands and uses the binomial theorem.

a.   Expands expressions of the form $(a + b)^n$ for small positive integer n.

b.   States the general form for the binomial coefficients for all positive integer n.

c.   Expands expressions of the form $(1 + x)^n$ where n takes positive, negative or fractional values.

d.   States the range of values of x for which the series is convergent.

e. Calculates the effect on the subject of a formula when one or more of the independent variables is subject to a small change or error.

8. EXPONENTIAL FUNCTION EXPANSIONS

Uses the series expansion of the exponential function.

a. States the expansion of e^x in a power series.

b. Deduces the expansion of e^{-x}.

c. States that the expansions are convergent for all x.

d. Deduces the expansion of ae^{kx} where k is positive or negative.

e. Deduces the series for e and evaluates e to four decimal places.

9. TRIGONOMETRIC OR CIRCULAR FUNCTIONS.

Sketches graphs of functions involving sine, cosine.

a. States the approximations $\sin x \approx \tan x \approx x$ and

$\cos x \approx 1 - \dfrac{x^2}{2}$ for small x.

b. Sketches graphs $\sin A$, $\sin 2A$, $2 \sin A$, $\sin \dfrac{A}{2}$

$\cos A$, $\cos 2A$, $2 \cos A$, $\cos \dfrac{A}{2}$ for values of A between $0°$ and $360°$.

c. Sketches graphs of $\sin^2 A$, $\cos^2 A$, for values of A between $0°$ and $360°$.

d. Sketches graphs of the functions in 9b and 9c where A is replaced by ωt.

e. Defines and identifies amplitude and frequency.

f. Defines angular velocity.

10. RESULTANT OF WAVES

Combines sine waves.

a.   Determines the single wave resulting from a combination of two waves of the same frequency using phasors and/or a graphical method.

b.   Defines the term phase angle.

c.   Measures the amplitude and phase angle of the resultant wave 10a.

d.   Determines graphically the single wave resulting from a combination of two waves, within the limitations of 10b. and 10c.

e.   Shows that the resultant of two sine waves of different frequencies gives rise to a non-sinusoidal, periodic function.

PART I

ALGEBRA III

EXPONENTIAL FUNCTIONS

AND NATURAL LOGARITHMS

1.   **Evaluates expressions involving exponentials and natural logarithms.**

a.   **Defines natural (Naperian) logarithms**

The logarithm of a number N to the base e is equal to x, that is
$\log_e N = x$ by the definition of a logarithm, the base e
when it is   raised to the power x gives the number N, that is
$e^x = N$ remember that

$$e = 1 + \frac{1}{1!} + \frac{1}{2!} + \frac{1}{3!} + \frac{1}{4!} + \ldots$$ to

infinite terms and this infinite series when it is summed up gives
the number 2.7182818 to eight significant figures $\log_e N = \ln N$.

WORKED EXAMPLE 1

(a)   Express the following in logarithmic form:

(i) $e^{2.35}$ = 10.49   (ii) e^{-3} = 0.0498

(iii) $e^{1/2}$ = 1.65   (iv) e^5 = 148.4

(v) e^2 = 7.389

(b)   Express the following in indicial form:

(i) $\log_e 452$ =   6.114   (ii) $\log_e 3.7 = 1.308$

(iii) $\log_e 0.25 = -1.386$ (iv) $\log_e 2$ = 0.693.

SOLUTION 1

(a)   (i) $e^{2.35} = 10.49$ $\log_e 10.49 = 2.35$

       (ii) $\ln 0.0498 = -3$

       (iii) $\ln 1.649 = 1/2$

       (iv) $\ln 148.4 = 5$

       (v) $\ln 7.389 = 2$

(b)   (i) $e^{6.114} = 452$ (ii) $e^{1.308} = 3.7$

       (iii) $e^{-1.386} = 0.25$ (iv) $e^{0.693} = 2.$

WORKED EXAMPLE 2

(a)   Express the following in logarithmic form:

       (i) $e^0 = 1$ (ii) $e^1 = e$ (iii) $e^{-1} = 0.368$

       (iv) $e^x = N.$

(b)   Express the following in indicial form:

       (i) $\ln 23.75 = 3.168$ (ii) $\ln 35,315 = 10.5$

       (iii) $\ln 1 = 0.$

SOLUTION 2

(a)   (i) $e^0 = 1$, hence $\ln 1 = 0$

       (ii) $e^1 = 2.718$, hence $\ln 2.718 = 1$

       (iii) $e^{-1} = 0.368$, hence $\ln 0.368 = -1$

       (iv) $e^x = N$, hence $\ln N = x.$

(b) $\ln 23.75 = 3.168,\ e^{3.168} = 23.75$

   $\ln 36,315 = 10.5\ \ e^{10.5} = 35,315$

   $\ln\ 1 = 0, = e^0 = 1.$

b.   **Determines natural (Naperian) logarithms from tables and by calculator,**

The natural logarithm or hyperbolic logarithm, $\log_e N$ is denoted by $\ln N$ which is found on most scientific calculators.

It is very easy to determine the natural logarithm of any positive number by calculator. The number whose logarithm is required is entered on the display of a calculator and then the 'ln' button is pressed giving the answer on the display.

$$\boxed{AC}\quad\boxed{2}\quad\boxed{\ln}\qquad = \ln 2 = 0.6931471,\ \ln 35 = 3.5553481$$

$\ln 0.59 = -0.5276327$, check these answers on your calculator.

$\log_e 2 = \ln 2 = 0.6931471$

by definition $e^{0.6931471} = 1.999998 = 2$ approximately

$\log_e 0.59 = -0.5276327$

by definition

$$e^{-0.5276327} = 0.59$$

$\log_e 35 = 3.555348$

by definition

$$e^{3.555348} = 35.$$

To obtain the latter answers, we use, '**INV**'or '2nd function' and then the 'ln' button in order to obtain e^x.

WORKED EXAMPLE 3

Practice with your calculator and find the logarithms to the base e of the following numbers:-

(i)   23.75   (ii) 2.95 (iii) 35,759 (iv) 267

(v)   0.999 and then inverse the procedure to obtain back the numbers.

SOLUTIONS 3

(i)   ln 23.75 = 3.1675825
(ii)   ln   2.95 = 1.0818052
(iii)   ln 35,759 = 10.484557
(iv)   ln 267   = 5.5872487
(v)   ln 0.999 = - 1.0005003x 10^{-3}.

It is observed that positive numbers below unity have negative logarithms and the logarithms of numbers above unity are positive and the logarithm of a negative number is not defined in the real world of numbers $\log_e$ (- 1) is not defined and the calculator registers the symbol **E** on the display indicating that there is an error.

c.   **States the relationship between common and natural (Naperian) logarithms.**

The logarithm of a number to the base 10 is called a common logarithm and it is denoted as $\log_{10} N$ or simply log N. In this case the base 10 is implied, it is the only base that can be omitted.

What is the relationship between $\log_{10} N$ and $\log_e N$?

$$\text{Let } y = \log_e N$$

by definition $e^y = N$ ...(1)
taking logarithms to the base 10 on both sides of the equation (1) we have

$$\log_{10} e^y = \log_{10} N$$

applying the rule that $\log a^n = n \log a$, we have

$$y \log_{10} e = \log_{10} N$$

$$y = \frac{\log_{10} N}{\log_{10} e} = \log_e N \qquad\qquad \ln N = \frac{\log_{10} N}{\log_{10} e}.$$

$$\log N = \log_{10} e \, \log_e N$$

$$\log N = 0.4342944 \, \ln N \quad ...(1)$$

the logarithm of the number N to the base 10 is expressed in terms of the logarithm of the number N to the base e.

From above $\ln N = (\log N) / 0,4342944$

$$\ln N = 2.3025851 \log N \text{ and therefore}$$

the logarithm of the number N to the base e is expressed in terms of the logarithm of the number N to the base 10.

d.   Uses natural (Naperian) logarithms to evaluate expressions arising in technological units.

CHARGING A CAPACITOR

The instantaneous value of voltage, v, or the voltage across a capacitor which is being charged through a resistor is given by the expression.

$$v = V(1 - e^{-t/\tau})$$

where $\tau = RC$.

WORKED EXAMPLE 4

If $v = 50$ volts, $V = 150$ volts and $\tau = 5$ ms determine the time taken t.

SOLUTION 4

$$v = V\left(1 - e^{-t/\tau}\right)$$

dividing both sides by V we have

$$\frac{v}{V} = 1 - e^{-t/\tau} \qquad e^{-t/\tau} = 1 - v/V \qquad e^{-t/\tau} = \frac{V - v}{V}$$

the reciprocal of each side $\quad e^{t/\tau} = \dfrac{V}{V - v}$

taking logarithms on both sides to the base e, we have

$$\ln e^{t/\tau} = \ln \dfrac{V}{V - v}$$

$$\dfrac{t}{\tau} \ln e = \ln \dfrac{V}{V - v}$$

$$\dfrac{t}{\tau} = \ln \dfrac{V}{V - v}$$

since $\ln e = 1$, $\log_e e = 1$ or $e^1 = e$ by definition

$$t = \tau \ln \dfrac{V}{V - v} = 5 \times 10^{-3} \ln \dfrac{150}{150 - 50}$$

$$= 5 \times 10^{-3} \ln \dfrac{150}{100} = 5 \times 10^{-3} \ln 1.5$$

$$= 5 \times 10^{-3} \times 0.4054651 = 2.03 \times 10^{-3} = 2.03$$

$$\tau = 2.03 \text{ ms.}$$

MAGNETISING A COIL

WORKED EXAMPLE 5

The instantaneous value of current i at $t = 1$ ms is 1 A, and the final value of current $I = 5$ A. Determine the time constant of the inductive circuit, given that $i = I (1 - e^{-t/\tau})$ where τ is the time constant.

SOLUTION 5

The growth of current is given by the equation

$$i = I (1 - e^{-t/\tau})$$

dividing both sides by I

$$\frac{i}{I} = 1 - e^{-t/\tau}$$

$$e^{-t/\tau} = 1 - \frac{i}{I}$$

$$e^{-t/\tau} = \frac{I - i}{I}$$

the reciprocal of each side

$$e^{t/\tau} = \frac{I}{I - i}$$

taking logarithms on both sides to the base e, we have

$$\ln e^{t/\tau} = \ln \frac{I}{I - i}$$

$$\frac{t}{\tau} \ln e = \ln \frac{I}{I - i}$$

but $\ln e = 1$

$$t = \tau \ln \frac{I}{I - i}$$

$$\tau = \frac{t}{\ln \dfrac{I}{I - i}}$$

$$\tau = \frac{10^{-3}}{\ln \dfrac{5}{5 - 1}}$$

$$\tau = \frac{10^{-3}}{\ln 1.25}$$

$$\tau = \frac{10^{-3}}{0.2231435}$$

$$\tau = 4.48 \times 10^{-3}$$

$$\tau = 4.48 \text{ ms.}$$

e.   **Solves equation involving e^x and $\ln x$.**

Let us consider an equation that contains terms such as e^x and e^{2x} such an equation is called an indicial or exponential equation.

WORKED EXAMPLE 6

Solve the equation $e^x + e^{-x} = 4$.

SOLUTION 6

$$e^x + e^{-x} = 4$$

multiplying each term by e^x,

$$e^{2x} + e^0 - 4\,e^x = 0.$$

Applying the laws of indices

$$e^{2x} + e^0 - 4\,e^x = 0$$

$$e^{2x} - 4\,e^x + 1 = 0.$$

If we replace $y = e^x$, the resulting equation becomes a quadratic equation

$$y^2 - 4y + 1 = 0$$

$$y = \frac{4 \pm \sqrt{16 - 4}}{2} = \frac{4 \pm \sqrt{12}}{2} = \frac{4 \pm 3.464}{2}$$

$$y = 3.732,\; y = 0.268$$

$$e^x = 3.732, \ln e^x = \ln 3.732,\; x = 1.317$$

$$e^x = 0.268, \ln e^x = \ln 0.268,\; x = -1.317.$$

WORKED EXAMPLE 7

Solve the logarithmic equation

$$\log_e x - \log_e \frac{1}{x+1} = 2$$

SOLUTION 7

Applying the rule $\log A - \log B = \log A/B$ the equation can be written as

$$\log_e x - \log_e \frac{1}{x+1} = 2$$

$$\log_e \frac{x}{1/(x+1)} = 2$$

$$\log_e x(x+1) = 2$$

by the definition of logarithm

$$e^2 = x(x+1)$$

$$x^2 + x - e^2 = 0$$

$$x = \frac{-1 \pm \sqrt{1 + 4e^2}}{2} = \frac{-1 \pm \sqrt{1 + 4 \times 7.3890561}}{2}$$

$$= \frac{-1 \pm 5.53}{2}$$

$$x = \frac{-1 + 5.53}{2}, \quad x = \frac{-1 - 5.53}{2}.$$

$$x = 2.264 \text{ or } x = -3.264.$$

EXERCISES 1

1. From the calculator find

   (i) $\log_e 1.234$ (ii) $\log_e 12.34$ (iii) $\log_e 1234$.

2. Find the numbers whose natural logarithms are

   (i) 4.174 (ii) 9.21   (iii) - 3.66.

3. The number of radioactive atoms present at a time $t = 0$, is N_0 and the number of radioactive atoms at the end of a time t, is N and these number related by the equation $N = N_0 e^{-\lambda t}$ where λ is the radioactivity decay constant.

   If $N = \dfrac{1}{2} N_0$ when $t = 1500$ years find the time when

   $$N = \dfrac{1}{20} N_0.$$

4. $e^{2x} - 5 e^x + 6 = 0$ is an indicial or exponential equation by substituting $y = e^x$, solve the equation for y and hence find the values of x.

5. Solve the equation $6 e^{2x} - 7 e^x + 2 = 0$.

6. If $i = I e^{-t/5 \times 0.001}$, $i = 3$ A, $I = 10$ A, determine t.

7. If $v = V (1 - e^{-t/5 \times 0.001})$

   If $t = 1 \times 10^{-3}$ s, $V = 100$ volts, determine v.

8. (i) If $v = V (1 - e^{-t/RC})$ and $R = 1$ and $C = 5, v = 1, V = 10$ determine the value of t.

   (ii) If $t = 1, RC = 1$ what is v if $V = 100$.

9. Calculate correct to three significant figures:-

   (i) $\dfrac{e^{0.3} - e^{0.3}}{2}$ (ii) $\dfrac{e^{0.5} + e^{-0.5}}{2}$ (iii) $6 \left(e^{0.8} - e^{-0.8} \right)$.

10. If $\log_e x = 5.95$ find x.

2. COMPLEX NUMBERS

EXTENDS THE NUMBER SYSTEM TO COMPLEX NUMBERS.

a.   Defines a complex number

b.   Plots complex numbers on an Argand diagram

c.   Determines the sum and difference of two complex numbers in the form $a + jb$, and relates results to Argand diagram.

d.   Determines the product of two complex numbers in the form $a + jb$.

e.   Defines the conjugate of a complex number.

f.   Uses 2e and evaluates $\dfrac{Z_1}{Z_2}$.

2a.   Definition of a complex number.

A complex number is a number which is not real. The square root of minus one, that is, $\sqrt{-1}$, is a complex number because there is no real number which can be multiplied by itself in order to give the answer of -1. The square roots of four, $\sqrt{4}$, however, are equal to ± 2 which are real numbers, because $2 \times 2 = 4$ or $(-2) \times (-2) = 4$.

Solving the quadratic equation $x^2 + x + 1 = 0$ we have

$$x = \frac{-1 \pm \sqrt{1 - 4 \times 1}}{2 \times 1} = \frac{-1 \pm \sqrt{-3}}{2} = -\frac{1}{2} \pm \frac{\sqrt{-3}}{2}.$$

THE J-NOTATION

The roots are $x_1 = -\dfrac{1}{2} + \dfrac{\sqrt{-3}}{2}$ and $x_2 = -\dfrac{1}{2} - \dfrac{\sqrt{-3}}{2}$

$$\sqrt{-3} = \sqrt{-1}\,\sqrt{3} = j\sqrt{3}$$

where $\sqrt{-1} = j$ and the roots can be expressed in terms of j

$$x_1 = -\frac{1}{2} + j\frac{\sqrt{3}}{2} \quad \text{and} \quad x_2 = -\frac{1}{2} - j\frac{\sqrt{3}}{2} \quad \text{and better still}$$

$$Z_1 = -\frac{1}{2} + j\frac{\sqrt{3}}{2} \quad \text{and} \quad Z_2 = -\frac{1}{2} - j\frac{\sqrt{3}}{2} \qquad \text{where}$$

Z denotes impedance.

In general $Z = x + jy$, the real term of Z is x and the imaginary term of Z is y, Re $Z = x$ and Im $Z = y$.

2b.   Plots complex numbers on an Argand diagram

An Argand diagram is a pair of cartesian axes, the y-axis and the x-axis.

The x-axis is the real axis and the y-axis is the imaginary axis.

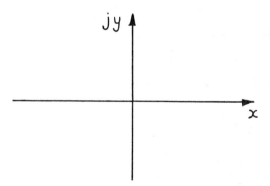

Fig. 1   ARGAND DIAGRAM

We can label the y axis by jy and the x-axis by x as shown in the diagram, **Fig. 1**.

$Z = x + jy, x$ and y are real quantities which can be either positive or negative.

WORKED EXAMPLE 8

Plot the complex numbers on an Argand diagram.

(i) $Z_1 = 3 + j4$ (ii) $Z_2 = 3 - j4$

(iii) $Z_3 = -3 + j4$ (iv) $Z_4 = -3 - j4$.

SOLUTION 8

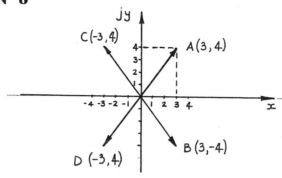

Fig. 2

Referring to **Fig. 2**.

We mark off three units along the positive x-axis and 4 units along the positive y-axis, the point **A** gives a pair of co-ordinates (3,4) and this is joined to the origin, **OA** represents the complex number Z_1, similarly **B** (3, -4) and **OB** represents the complex number Z_2, **OC** = Z_3 and **OD** = Z_4.

THE ARGAND DIAGRAM IS VERY IMPORTANT DIAGRAM

In order to locate the complex number in the correct quadrant and read off the position from the reference **OX** which is zero degrees, **OY**, the positive y-axis is 90° - **OX**, the negative x-axis is 180° and **OY**, the negative y-axis is 270° all measured in an anti-clockwise direction. Complex numbers are vectors, that is, possess a magnitude and direction.

19

2c.   **Determines the sum and difference of two complex numbers in the form** $a + jb$, **and relates results to Argand diagram.**

Consider two complex numbers

$$Z_1 = x_1 + j y_1 \text{ and } Z_2 = x_2 + jy_2$$

to find the sum $Z_1 + Z_2$, we add the real terms separately and we add the imaginary terms separately

$$Z_1 + Z_2 = x_1 + jy_1 + x_2 + jy_2 = (x_1 + x_2) + j (y_1 + y_2).$$

The difference of the complex numbers is given

by $Z_1 - Z_2 = (x_1 + jy_1) - (x_2 + jy_2)$

$$= (x_1 - x_2) + j (y_1 - y_2).$$

The sum and difference can be easily found in the cartesian form of the complex numbers $(Z = x + jy)$.

To the vector sum or vector difference a parallelgram is formed as shown below in the worked example.

WORKED EXAMPLE 9

Find the sum $Z_1 + Z_2$ and the difference $Z_1 - Z_2$ of the two complex numbers $Z_1 = 2 + j5$ and $Z_2 = 4 + j2$.

(i)   Algebraically.

(ii)   Vectorially or graphically on an Argand diagram.

SOLUTION 9

(i) $Z_1 + Z_2 = 2 + j5 + 4 + j2 = 6 + j7$

$Z_1 + Z_2 = 2 + j5 - 4 - j2 = -2 + j3.$

(ii)

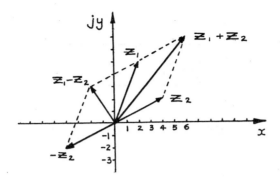

Fig. 3

2d. THE PRODUCT OF TWO COMPLEX NUMBERS

If $Z_1 = x_1 + jy_1$ and $Z_2 = x_2 + jy_2$ the product

$$Z_1 Z_2 = (x_1 + jy_1)(x_2 + jy_2)$$

$$= x_1 x_2 + jy_1 x_2 + jx_1 y_2 + j^2 y_1 y_2$$

$$= (x_1 x_2 - y_1 y_2) + j(y_1 x_2 + x_1 y_2)$$

where $j^2 = -1$.

WORKED EXAMPLE 10

Determine the products

(i) $Z_1 Z_2$ (ii) $Z_1 Z_3$ (iii) $Z_2 Z_3$ if $Z_1 = -3 - j4, Z_2 = 2 - j3, Z_3 = -3 + j5$.

SOLUTION 10

(i) $\quad Z_1 Z_2 = (-3 - j4)(2 - j3) = -6 - j8 + 9j + j^2 12$
$\quad\quad\quad = -6 - 12 + j = -18 + j$

$$\boxed{Z_1 Z_2 = -18 + j}$$

(ii) $\quad Z_1 Z_3 = (-3 - j4)(-3 + j5) = 9 + j12 - j15 - j^2 20 = 9 + 20 - j3$

21

$$\boxed{Z_1 Z_3 = 29 - j3}$$

(iii) $Z_2 Z_3 = (2 - j3) \ \ (- 3 + j5) = - 6 \ + j9 + j10 - j^2 \ 15$

$$\boxed{Z_2 Z_3 = 9 + j19}$$

2e.   THE CONJUGATE OF A COMPLEX NUMBER

If $Z = x + jy$, Z^* or $\overline{Z}$ is the conjugate of Z (Z^* (Z - star)) or

($\overline{Z}$ (Z bar) $\overline{Z} = x - jy$.

The real term remains unaltered the imaginary term changes sign.

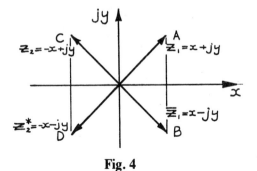

Fig. 4

The x-axis is used as a mirror in which we see the image of **A** is **B** a mirror image of **C** is **D** and vice - versa, the image mirror of $Z_1 = x - jy$ is $Z = x + jy$ and image mirror of $Z_2^* = - x - jy$ is $Z_2^{**} = - x + jy$.

The conjugate is used in the next topic in evaluating as quotient $\dfrac{Z_1}{Z_2}$.

2f EVALUATES Z_1/Z_2 USING THE CONJUGATE TECHNIQUE

If $Z_1 = x_1 + jy_1$ and $Z_2 = x_2 + jy_2$, the quotient $\dfrac{Z_1}{Z_2} = \dfrac{x_1 + jy_1}{x_2 + jy_2}$.

In order to divide two complex numbers we need to multiply the numerator and denominator by the conjugate of the denominator, which is $x_2 + jy_2$

$$\frac{Z_1}{Z_2} = \frac{(x_1 + jy_1)}{(x_2 + jy_2)} \times \frac{(x_2 - jy_2)}{(x_2 - jy_2)} = \frac{x_1 x_2 + jy_1 x_2 - jx_1 y_2 + y_1 y_2}{x_2^2 - j^2 y_2^2}$$

$$= \frac{(x_1 x_2 + y_1 y_2) + j(y_1 x_2 - x_1 y_2)}{x_2^2 + y_2^2}$$

remember $(a + b)(a - b) = (a^2 - b^2)$ is the difference of squares also observe that the denominator is now a positive real quantity.

WORKED EXAMPLE 11

If $Z_1 = -3 - j4$, $Z_2 = 2 - j3$, $Z_3 = -3 + j5$

Determine (i) $\dfrac{Z_1}{Z_2}$ (ii) $\dfrac{Z_2}{Z_1}$ (iii) $\dfrac{Z_3}{Z_3}$ (iv) $\dfrac{Z_3}{Z_1}$ using the conjugate technique.

SOLUTION 11

(i) $\dfrac{Z_1}{Z_3} = \dfrac{-3 - 4j}{2 - 3j} \times \dfrac{2 + 3j}{2 + 3j} = \dfrac{-6 - 8j - 9j + 12}{4 + 9} = \dfrac{6}{13} - \dfrac{17}{13}j$

(ii) $\dfrac{Z_2}{Z_1} = \dfrac{(2 - 3j)}{(-3 - 4j)} \times \dfrac{(-3 + 4j)}{(-3 + j4)} = \dfrac{-6 + 9j + 8j + 12}{(-3)^2 + 4^2} = \dfrac{6}{25} + \dfrac{17j}{25}$

(iii) $\dfrac{Z_2}{Z_3} = \dfrac{(2 - 3j)}{(-3 + 5j)} \times \dfrac{-3 - 5j}{-j - 5j} = \dfrac{-6 + 9j - 10j + 15j^2}{(-3)^2 - j^2 25} = \dfrac{-21 - 1j}{34}$

(iv) $\dfrac{Z_3}{Z_1} = \dfrac{(-3 + 5j)}{(-3 - 4j)} \times \dfrac{(-3 + 4j)}{(-3 + 4j)} = \dfrac{9 - 15j - 12j - 20}{9 + 16} = -\dfrac{11}{25} - \dfrac{27}{25}j.$

23

EXERCISES 2

1. Write the following in complex number notation:

    (i) $\sqrt{-2}$　(ii) $\sqrt{-4}$　(iii) $\sqrt{-8}$　(iv) $\sqrt{-16}$　(v) $\sqrt{-27}$.

2. Determine whether the following quadratic equations have real or complex roots and find the roots

    (i)　$3x^2 - x + 1 = 0$
    (ii) $x^2 - 4x + 8 = 0$
    (iii) $x^2 + 2x + 2 = 0$
    (iv) $-5x^2 + 7x + 5 = 0$
    (v)　$-x^2 + x - 5 = 0$.

3. Express the following points of co-ordinates in the complex number form:

    (i)　A (1,3) (ii)　E (- 1,3), (iii)　F (2, - 4) (iv)　J (- 3, - 4).

4. Express the following complex numbers in the form of points of coordinates:

    (i)　$Z_1 = 3 + j4$ (ii) $Z_2 = 3 - j4$ (iii) $Z_3 = - 3 + j4$ (iv) $Z_4 = -3 - j4$.

5. Plot the complex numbers in (4) in an Argand diagram.

6. (i)　If Re $Z = x$ and Im $Z = y$, write down the value of Z.

    (ii)　If Re $Z = - 3$ and Im $Z = 5$, write down the value of Z.

7. (a)　Find the sum and difference of the vectors

    $E_1 = 20 + j30$ and $E_2 = 10 + j15$.

    (b)　Find the product and the quotient of the complex numbers E_1 and E_2, that is, $E_1 E_2$ and E_1/E_2.

8. Express in the form $a + jb$ the following:-

    (i) $(3j)$ $(5j)$ (ii) $(4 - 5j)$ $(1 + j)$ (iii) $(1 + j)$ $(1 - j)$ (iv) $(4 + 3j)^2$
    (iv) $(1 - j^2)^2$.

9. Express the following operations in the form $a + jb$:

If $Z_1 = 3 - 4j, Z_2 = 1 + j, Z_3 = 2 + 3j$

(i) $Z_1 Z_2$ (ii) $Z_1 Z_3$ (iii) $Z_1 Z_2 Z_3$.

10. If a complex number $Z = x + jy$ and its conjugate

$Z^* = x - jy$, show that (i) $ZZ^* = x^2 + y^2$ and

(ii) $\left(\dfrac{1}{Z}\right)^* = \dfrac{1}{Z^*}$.

3. MODULUS AND ARGUMENT OF COMPLEX NUMBERS

Understands the modulus, argument form of complex numbers

a. Converts $a + jb$ into polar form and vice-versa.

   Relates j to an operator and shows that j can be regarded as $\sqrt{-1}$.

b. Defines the modulus and argument of a complex number.

c. Multiplies and divides complex numbers using the polar form.

d. Determines the square roots of a complex number.

POLAR FORM OF A COMPLEX NUMBER.

MODULUS

$Z = x + jy$

the modulus of Z is denoted $|Z|$
and means the magnitude of the complex number Z

$$|Z| = \sqrt{(x)^2 + (y)^2}$$

note that the real term is squared and the imaginary term (y) is squared

25

and <u>not</u> the j.

The hypotenuse of the right angled triangle with sides x and y is the modulus of Z.

$$|Z| = \sqrt{x^2 + y^2} = r$$

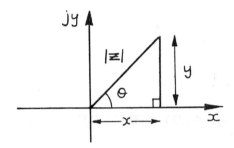

Fig. 5

ARGUMENT

The argument of Z is the angle of Z measured in an anti clockwise direction from the reference line ox (0°) arg Z is the notation for the argument of Z
$\tan \Theta = y/x$ arg $Z = \Theta = \tan^{-1} (y/x)$ the inverse function of the tangent arg $Z = \Theta = \tan^{-1} (y/x)$.

To avoid error in evaluating the angle of the complex number, it is necessary to display the complex number on an Argand diagram.

$Z = x + jy = r \cos \Theta + jr \sin \Theta = r (\cos \Theta + j \sin \Theta)$.

The polar form of $Z = x + jy$ is $Z = r (\cos \Theta + j \sin \Theta)$, $\cos \Theta + j \sin \Theta$ can be replaced by the abbreviation $\underline{/\Theta} = \cos \Theta + j \sin \Theta$
$\underline{/-\Theta} = \cos \Theta - j \sin \Theta$.

WORKED EXAMPLE 12

Determine the moduli and arguments of the following complex numbers:

(i) $Z_1 = 3j$ (ii) $Z_2 = 5$ (iii) $Z_3 = -2 + j3$ (iv) $Z_4 = \cos \Phi - j \sin \Phi$.

SOLUTION 12

(i) $Z_1 = 3j$ $\quad |Z_1| = \sqrt{0 + 3^2} = 3$ $\quad$ arg $Z_1 = \tan^{-1} \dfrac{3}{0} = 90°$

(ii) $Z_2 = 5,$ $\quad \left|Z_2\right| = 5$ $\quad$ arg $Z_2 = 0°$

(iii) $Z_3 = -2 + j3$ $\quad |Z_3| = \sqrt{(-2)^2 + 3^2} = \sqrt{4 + 9} = \sqrt{13}$

$\quad\quad\quad$ arg $Z_3 = 180 - \tan^{-1} 3/2 = 123.7°$

(iv) $Z_4 = \cos\Phi - j\sin\Phi$ $\quad \left|Z_4\right| = \sqrt{\cos^2\Phi + (-\sin\Phi)^2} = 1$

$\quad\quad\quad\quad\quad\quad\quad\quad$ arg $Z_4 = -\Phi.$

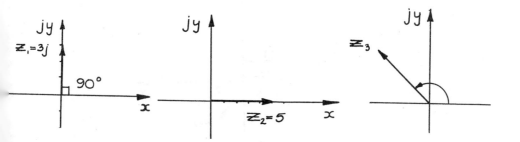

Fig. 6 $\quad\quad\quad\quad\quad\quad$ Fig. 7 $\quad\quad\quad\quad\quad\quad$ Fig. 8

WORKED EXAMPLE 13

Determine the polar forms of the complex numbers:

(i) $\quad Z_1 = -3 + j4$ (ii) $Z_2 = 2 - j3$ (iii) $Z_3 = -3 + j5$.

SOLUTION 13

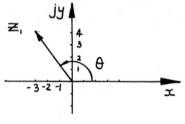

Fig. 9

(i)
$$\left| Z_1 \right| = \sqrt{(-3)^2 + (\ 4)^2} = \sqrt{9 + 16} = 5$$
$$arg\, Z_1 = 180° - \tan^{-1} \frac{4}{3}$$
$$= 126° \ 52' = \Theta$$

$Z_1 = 5 (\cos 126° \ 52' + j \sin 126° \ 52')$

$Z_1 = 5 \,\underline{/\ 126° \ 52'}.$

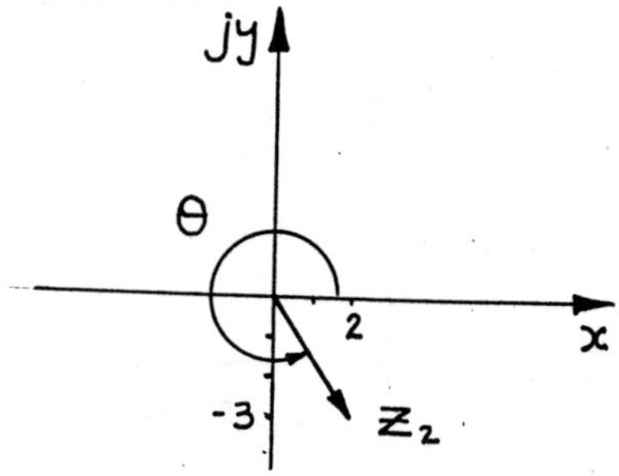

Fig. 10

$Z_2 = 2 - j\, 3$

(ii)
$$\left| Z_2 \right| = \sqrt{2^2 + (-3)^2} = \sqrt{13}$$

$$arg\, Z_2 = 360° - \tan^{-1} 3/2$$
$$= 360° - 56° 18' 35''$$
$$= 303° 41'.$$

$$Z_2 = \sqrt{13} \; \underline{/\; 303°41'}$$

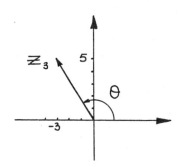

Fig. 11

(iii)
$$Z_3 = -3 + j\,5$$

$$\left| Z_3 \right| = \sqrt{(-3)^2 + 5^2} = \sqrt{34}$$

$$\arg Z_3 = 180° - \tan^{-1}\frac{5}{3} = 180° - 59°\,2'\,10''$$

$$= 120°57' = \Theta$$

$$Z_3 = \sqrt{34} \; \underline{/\; 120°57'}$$

3c MULTIPLICATION AND DIVISION OF COMPLEX NUMBERS USING POLAR FORM

MULTIPLICATION of complex numbers using polar form.

$$Z_1 = r_1 \underline{/\; \Theta_1} \qquad Z_2 = r_2 \underline{/\; \Theta_2}$$

$$Z_1\, Z_2 = r_1\, r_2 \underline{/\; \Theta_1 + \Theta_2}$$

the moduli are multiplied and the arguments are added.

WORKED EXAMPLE 14

If $Z_1 = 3 \angle 45°$, $Z_2 = 4 \angle 65°$, $Z_3 = 5 \angle 90°$.
Determines (i) $Z_1 Z_3$ (ii) $Z_1 Z_2$ (iii) $Z_2 Z_3$ in (a) polar form and (b) cartesian form.

SOLUTION 14

(a) (i) $Z_1 Z_3 = (3 \angle 45°)(5 \angle 90°) = 15 \angle 135°$

(ii) $Z_1 Z_2 = (3 \angle 45°)(4 \angle 65°) = 12 \angle 110°$

(iii) $Z_2 Z_3 = (4 \angle 65°)(5 \angle 90°) = 20 \angle 155°$

(b)

(i) $Z_1 Z_3 = (\cos 135°) + j \sin 135°)$

$$Z_1 Z_3 = -\frac{15}{\sqrt{2}} + \frac{15}{\sqrt{2}} j$$

(ii) $Z_1 Z_2 = 12 (\cos 110° + j \sin 110°) = -4.1 + j11.3$

(iii) $Z_2 Z_3 = 20 \angle 155° = 20 (\cos 155° + j \sin 155°)$

$Z_2 Z_3 = -18.1 + j 8.45$.

Division of complex numbers using the polar form.

$$Z_1 = r_1 \angle \theta_1 \qquad Z_2 = r_2 \angle \theta_2$$

$$\frac{Z_1}{Z_2} = \frac{r_1 \angle \theta_1}{r_2 \angle \theta_2} = \frac{r_1}{r_2} \angle \theta_1 - \theta_2$$

$$\frac{Z_2}{Z_1} = \frac{r_2 \angle \theta_2}{r_1 \angle \theta_1} = \frac{r_2}{r_1} \angle \theta_2 - \theta_1.$$

The division is performed by dividing the moduli and substracting the arguments.

WORKED EXAMPLE 15

If $Z_1 = 25 \underline{/\ \pi/3}$ $Z_2 = 5 \underline{/\ \pi/6}$ $Z_3 = 1 \underline{/\ \pi/4}$.

Determine (i) Z_1/Z_2 (ii) Z_1/Z_3 (iii) Z_2/Z_1 (iv) Z_3/Z_2 in (a) polar form and in (b) cartesian form.

SOLUTION 15

$$\frac{Z_1}{Z_2} = \frac{25 \underline{/\ \pi/3}}{5 \underline{/\ \pi/6}} = 5 \underline{/\ \pi/3 - \pi/6} = 5 \underline{/\ \pi/6}$$

(a)   (i)

$$\frac{Z_1}{Z_3} = \frac{25 \underline{/\ \pi/3}}{1 \underline{/\ \pi/4}} = 25 \underline{/\ \pi/3 - \pi/4} = 25 \underline{/\ \pi/12}$$

(ii)

$$\frac{Z_2}{Z_1} = \frac{5 \underline{/\ \pi/6}}{25 \underline{/\ \pi/3}} = \frac{1}{5} \underline{/\ \pi/6 - \pi/3} = \frac{1}{5} \underline{/\ -\pi/6}$$

(iii)

$$\frac{Z_1}{Z_2} = \frac{1 \underline{/\ \pi/4}}{5 \underline{/\ \pi/6}} = \frac{1}{5} \underline{/\ \pi/4 - \pi/6} = \frac{1}{5} \underline{/\ \pi/12} \ .$$

(iv)

$$\frac{Z_1}{Z_2} = 5 \underline{/\pi/6} = 5(\cos \pi/_6 + j \sin \pi/_6) = 5 (0.866 + j\,0.5)$$

$$= 4.33 + j\,2.5$$

(b)   (i)

$$\frac{Z_1}{Z_3} = 25 \underline{/\pi/12} = 25 (\cos \pi/12 + j \sin \pi/12)$$

$$= 24.2 + j\,6.47$$

(ii)

(iii) $$\frac{Z_1}{Z_1} = \frac{1}{5} \underline{/\pi/6} = 0.2 (\cos \pi/6 - j \sin \pi/6) = 0.173 - 0.1$$

(iv) $$\frac{Z_3}{Z_2} = \frac{1}{5} \underline{/\ \pi/12} \doteq 0.2 (\cos \pi/12 + j \sin \pi/12)$$

$$= 0.193 + j\,0.052.$$

3d.   The square roots of a complex number

Let $Z = x + jy$.

The square roots of this complex number are complex numbers, since $x + jy = (a + bj)^2$ then $\sqrt{x + jy} = \pm (a + jb)$ where a and b are real quantities, squaring up both sides.

$$x + jy = (a + jb)^2 = a^2 + j^2 b^2 + 2 jba = a^2 - b^2 + j2\,ab.$$

Equating the real and imaginary terms, we have $x = a^2 - b^2 \ldots (1)$ and $y = 2\,ab \ldots (2)$ substituting (2) in (1) we have $b = y/2a$, $x = a^2 - (y/2a)^2$.

$$x = a^2 - \frac{y^2}{4a^2}$$

$$4a^4 - 4\,a^2 x - y^2 = 0$$

which is a quartic equation in a

$$a^2 = \frac{4x \pm \sqrt{16x^2 + 16y^2}}{8} = \frac{1}{2} x \pm \frac{1}{2} \sqrt{x^2 + y^2}$$

$$a = \pm \sqrt{\frac{1}{2}\left(x \pm \sqrt{x^2 + y^2}\right)}$$

$$a = \pm \sqrt{\frac{1}{2}\left(x + \sqrt{x^2 + y^2}\right)}$$

since the other value is not valid

$$a = \pm \sqrt{\frac{1}{2}\left(x - \sqrt{x^2 + y^2}\right)}$$

$$b = \frac{y}{2a} = \frac{y}{2\left[\pm\sqrt{\frac{1}{2}\left(x + \sqrt{x^2 + y^2}\right)}\right]} = \pm \frac{y}{2\sqrt{\frac{1}{2}\left(x + \sqrt{x^2 + y^2}\right)}}$$

otherwise a shall be a complex number.

The theory above seems to be somehow complex and tedious.

WORKED EXAMPLE 16

Determine the square roots of $3 + j4$.

SOLUTION 16

The square roots of $3 + j4$ are where a and b are real squaring up both sides
$3 + j4 = (a + jb)^2 = a^2 - b^2 + j2ab$.

Equating real and imaginary terms

$$a^2 - b^2 = 3 \quad \ldots \quad (1)$$
$$2ab = 4 \quad \ldots \quad (2)$$

From (2) $b = 4/2a = \dfrac{2}{a}$ and substituting in (i) $a^2 - \dfrac{4}{a^2} = 3$

or $a^4 - 3\,a^2 - 4 = 0$

solving for a^2, $a^2 = \dfrac{3 \pm \sqrt{9 + 16}}{2} = \dfrac{3 \pm 5}{2}$

$a^2 = 4$ and $a^2 = -1$ the latter is not valid since a must be a real quantity, hence $a = \pm 2$ and $b = \pm 1$. If $a = 2$, $b = 1$, if $a = -2$, $b = -1$.

WORKED EXAMPLE 17

Determine the square roots of j.

SOLUTION 17

Let $\sqrt{j} = \pm (a + jb)$, squaring up both sides, $j = a^2 - b^2 + j\,2ab$, equating real and imaginary terms, $a^2 - b^2 = 0$ and $2ab = 1$ or $b = 1/2a$ but

$$a^2 - \frac{1}{(2a)^2} = 0, \quad 4\,a^4 = 1, \quad a^2 = \pm \frac{1}{2} \quad \text{only} \quad a^2 = \frac{1}{2}$$

is valid or $a = \pm 1/\sqrt{2}$.

If $a = 1\sqrt{2}$, $b = \dfrac{1}{2}\sqrt{2} = \dfrac{\sqrt{2}}{2}\dfrac{\sqrt{2}}{\sqrt{2}} = \dfrac{1}{\sqrt{2}}$ and if

$a = -1/\sqrt{2}$, $b = \dfrac{1}{-2/\sqrt{2}} = -\dfrac{1}{\sqrt{2}}$.

Therefore $\sqrt{j} = \pm \left(\dfrac{1}{\sqrt{2}} + j\dfrac{1}{\sqrt{2}} \right)$.

The square roots of j are $\dfrac{1}{\sqrt{2}} + j\,\dfrac{1}{\sqrt{2}}$ and $-\dfrac{1}{\sqrt{2}} - \dfrac{j1}{\sqrt{2}}$.

APPLICATION OF COMPLEX NUMBERS IN A.C. THEORY

Applies complex numbers to a.c. quantities.

Identifies complex numbers with phasor quantities.

Solves simple a.c. circuit problems using complex numbers e.g. (a) R, L, and C in series combination (b) R, L, and C in parallel combination

Identifies complex numbers with phasor quantities.

The current through a resistor and the voltage across a resistor are in phase.

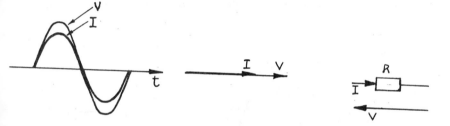

Fig. 12

$$R = \frac{V}{I} = \frac{V \underline{/\,0^\circ}}{I \underline{/\,0^\circ}} = \frac{V}{I} \underline{/\,0^\circ}.$$

The current through a pure inductor and the voltage across the inductor are 90° out of phase, the current lags the voltage by 90°.

$$X_L = \frac{V_L}{I_L} = \frac{V_L \underline{/\,90^\circ}}{I_L \underline{/\,0^\circ}} = \frac{V_L}{I_L} \underline{/\,90^\circ} = \omega L \underline{/\,90^\circ}.$$

Therefore X_L, the inductive reactance can be represented in complex numbers as

$$X_L = j\omega L.$$

35

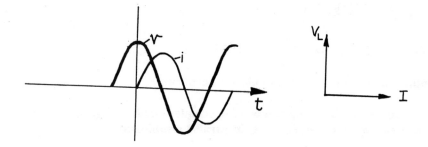

Fig. 13

The current through a capacitor and the voltage across the capacitor are 90° out of phase, the current leads the voltage by 90°.

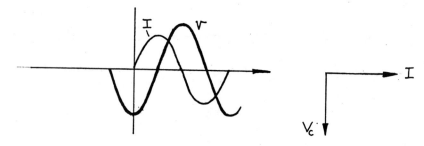

Fig. 14

$$X_c = \frac{V_c}{I} = -j\frac{V_c}{I} = -jX_c = -j\frac{1}{\omega C}\frac{j}{j} = \frac{1}{j\omega C}$$

$$X_c = \frac{1}{j\omega C}$$

Solves simple a.c. circuit problems using complex numbers

(a)   The impedance of the a.c. circuit can be written in complex numbers

$$Z = R + j\omega L + \frac{1}{j\omega C}$$

36

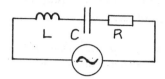

Fig. 15

$$V = 30 \, \underline{/\,30°} \quad \text{volts}$$

$$f = 1000 \text{ Hz.}$$

WORKED EXAMPLE 18

If the supply voltage is given as $30 \, \underline{/\,30°}$ volts and $R = 10 \, \Omega$, $C = 20 \, \mu\text{F}$, $L = 0.5$ H. Calculate the current in the circuit.

SOLUTION 18

$$I = \frac{V}{Z} = \frac{30 \, \underline{/\,30°}}{620.4 \, \underline{/\,89° 5'}} = 48.3 \, \underline{/\,-59° 5'} \quad \text{mA}$$

$$Z = R + j \, 2\pi f L + \frac{1}{j \, 2\pi f C} = 10 + j \, 2\pi 1000 \, (0.5) + \frac{10^6}{j \, 2\pi 1000 \times 20}$$

$$Z = 10 + j \, 628.3 - j \, 7.96 = 10 + j \, 620.34$$

$$|Z| = \sqrt{10^2 \, (628.3 - 7.96)^2} = 620.4 \, \Omega$$

$$\arg Z = \tan^{-1} \frac{620.34}{10} = 89° \, 5'.$$

37

WORKED EXAMPLE 19

A capacitor is connected in series with a resistor and the combination is connected across an a.c. supply voltage of 240 $\underline{/\ 0°}$ volts.

If C = 100 μF, R = 50 Ω and f = 50 Hz. Determine the magnitude and argument of the impedance and hence calculate the current in polar form.

SOLUTION 19

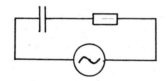

Fig. 16

240 $\underline{/0}°$ volts

f = 50 Hz

$$Z = R + \frac{1}{j\omega C} = 50 + \frac{1}{2j\pi(50\ (100)\ x\ 10^{-6}}$$

$$= 50 + 31.83j$$

$$|Z| = \sqrt{50^2 + (-31.83)^2} = 59.3\,\Omega$$

$$\arg Z = -\tan^{-1} 31.83/50 = -32.5°$$

$$Z = 59.3\underline{/-32.5°}\ \Omega$$

$$I = \frac{V}{Z} = \frac{240\ \underline{/\ 0°}}{59.3\ \underline{/\ -32.5°}} = 4.05\underline{/\ 32.5°}.\ \text{A}.$$

(b) **TO DETERMINE THE IMPEDANCE OF THE A.C. CIRCUITS.**

(i) $Z = \dfrac{R\,(j\omega L)}{R + j\omega L}$

Fig. 17

(ii) $Z = \dfrac{R\left(\dfrac{1}{j\omega C}\right)}{R + \dfrac{1}{j\omega C}} = \dfrac{R}{j\omega CR + 1} = \dfrac{R}{1 + j\omega CR}$

Fig. 18

(iii) $Z = \dfrac{(j\omega L)\left(\dfrac{1}{j\omega C}\right)}{j\omega L + \dfrac{1}{j\omega C}} = \dfrac{j\omega L}{(j\omega L)\,(j\omega C) + 1} = \dfrac{j\omega L}{1 - \omega^2 LC}$

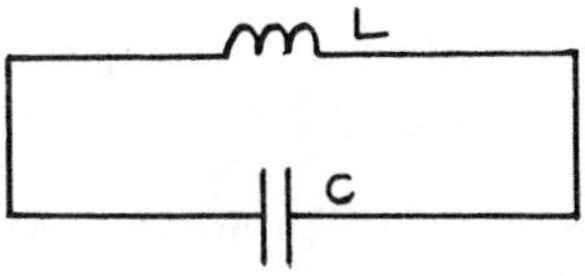

Fig. 19

(iv) $\dfrac{1}{Z} = \dfrac{1}{R} + j\omega C + \dfrac{1}{j\omega L}$

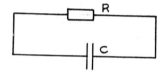

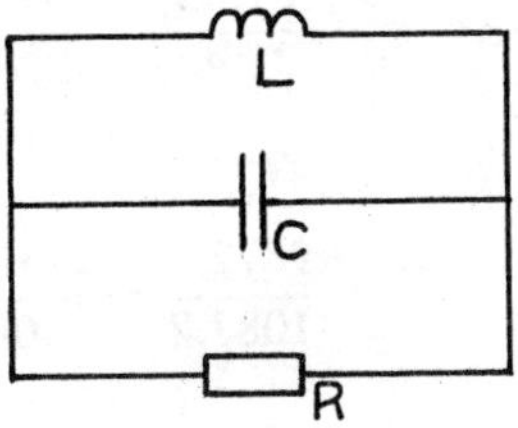

Fig. 20

(v) $\dfrac{1}{Z} = j\omega C + \dfrac{1}{R + j\omega L}$

39

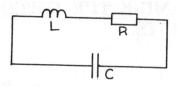

Fig. 21

WORKED EXAMPLE 20

For the circuit diagrams shown, if $R = 10 \, \Omega$, $L = 50$ mH, $C = 100 \, \mu$F and $f = 100$ Hz, determine the impedance of each circuit in cartesian and polar forms.

SOLUTION 20

(i)

$$Z = j \frac{R\omega L}{R + J\omega L} = j \frac{(10) \, 2\pi \, 100) \, (0.05)}{10 + j \, 2\pi \, 100 \, (0.05)} = \frac{314.2j}{10 + 31.42j}$$

$$Z = \frac{314.2j}{10 \times 31.42j} \times \frac{10 - 31.42j}{10 - 31.42j} = \frac{3142j + 9872.2}{100 + 987.2}$$

$$Z = \frac{9872.2}{1087.2} + j \frac{3142}{1087.2} = 9.08 + 2.89j$$

$$Z = (9.08 + j \, 2.89) \, \Omega$$

$$| \, Z \, | = \sqrt{9.08^2 + 2.89^2} = 9.53 \, \Omega$$

$$\arg Z = \tan^{-1} \frac{2.89}{9.08} = 17.7°$$

$$Z = 9.53 \, \underline{/ \, 17.7°} \, \Omega \, .$$

(ii)

$$Z = \frac{R}{1 + j \, \omega CR} = \frac{10}{1 + j \, 2\pi \, (100) \, 100 \, x \, 10^{-6} \, 10} = \frac{10}{1 + j \, 0.628}$$

$$Z = \frac{10 \, (1 - j \, 0.628)}{(1 + j \, 0.628)(1 - j \, 0.628)} = \frac{10}{1.39} - j \, \frac{6.28}{1.39} = 7.17 - j \, 4.52$$

$$Z = (7.17 - j \, 4.52) \, \Omega$$

$$| \, Z \, | = \sqrt{7.17^2 + (-4.52)^2} = 8.48$$

$$\arg Z = -\tan^{-1} \frac{4.52}{7.17} = -32.2°$$

$$Z = 8.48 \, \underline{/ \, -32.2°} \, \Omega \, .$$

(iii)

$$Z = \frac{j\omega L}{1 - \omega^2 LC} = \frac{j \, 2\pi \, 100 \, (0.05)}{1 - 4\pi^2 \, 10,000 \, 0.05 \, x \, 100 \, x \, 10^{-6}} = \frac{j \, 2\pi 100 \, (0.05)}{-0.974}$$

$$Z = j \frac{31.4}{0.974} = j\ 32.3, \ |Z| = 32.3, \ \text{arg } Z = \underline{/\ -90°},$$

$$Z = 32.3 \underline{/\ -90°} \ \Omega \ .$$

(iv)

$$\frac{1}{Z} = \frac{1}{10} + j\ 2\pi\ 100\ x\ 100\ x\ 10^{-6} + \frac{1}{j\ 2\pi\ 100\ 0.05} \frac{j}{j}$$

$$\frac{1}{Z} = \frac{1}{10} + j\ 0.0628 - j\ 31.42$$

$$\frac{1}{Z} = 0.1 - j\ 31.4$$

$$Z = \frac{1}{0.1 - j\ 31.4} \ x \ \frac{0.1 + j\ 31.4}{0.1 + j\ 31.4} = \frac{0.1 + j\ 31.4}{0.1^2 + 31.4^2}$$

$$Z = \frac{0.1}{985.97} + j\ \frac{31.4}{985.97} = 0.0001 + j\ 0.032$$

$$Z = (0.0001 + j0.032)\ \Omega$$

$|Z| = 0.032$ $\text{arg } Z = \tan^{-1} 0.032\backslash 0.0001 = 89.8°$

$$Z - 0.032 \underline{/\ 89.8°} \ \Omega \ .$$

(v)

$$\frac{1}{Z} = j\ 2\pi\ 100\ x\ 100\ x\ 10^{-6} + \frac{1}{10 + j\ 2\pi\ 100\ x\ 0.05}$$

$$= j\ 0.0628 + \frac{1}{10 + j\ 31.4}$$

$$\frac{1}{Z} = \frac{j\,0.628 - 0.0628 \times 31.4 + 1}{10 + j\,31.4}$$

$$= \frac{-0.972 + j\,0.628}{10 + j\,31.4}$$

$$Z = \frac{10 + j\,31.4}{-0.972 + j\,0.628}$$

$$= \frac{(10 + j\,31.4)\,(-0.772 - j\,0.628)}{(-0.972 + j\,0.628)\,(-0.972j\,0.628)}$$

$$Z = \frac{-9.72 - j\,30.5 - j\,6.28 + 19.72}{1.34}$$

$$= \frac{10}{1.34} - j\,\frac{36.78}{1.34} = 7.46 - j\,27.4$$

$$Z = (7.46 - j\,27.4)\,\Omega \quad |\,Z\,| = 39.5 \arg Z = -\tan^{-1} 27.4\backslash7.46 = -74.8°$$

$$Z = 39.5\underline{/\,^{-74.8°}}.$$

WORKED EXAMPLE 21

The r.m.s. voltage, V, is given by the complex number $V = 3 + j4$ and the r.m.s. current, I, is given by the complex number $I = 1 - j2$. Determine the moduli and arguments on V and I and hence find the phase angle between V and I. If the power in the circuit is given by the expression $P = |\,I\,|\,|\,V\,|\,\cos \Phi$ where Φ is the phase angle between V and I, find the power in watts.

SOLUTION 21

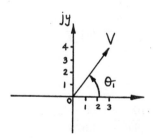

Fig. 22

$V = 3 + j4$

$|V| = \sqrt{3^2 + 4^2} = \sqrt{9 + 16} = \sqrt{25} = 5$

$\arg V = \tan^{-1} 4/3 = 53° \, 7' \, 48.3'' = 53.13° = \theta_1$

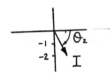

Fig. 23

$I = 1 - j2$

$|I| = \sqrt{1^2 + (-2)^2} = \sqrt{1 + 4} = \sqrt{5}$

$\arg I = -\tan^{-1} 2/1 = -63° \, 26' \, 5.8'' = -63.44° = -\theta_2$

$\Phi = \text{phase angle} = \theta_1 - (-\theta_2) = \theta_1 + \theta_2 = 53.13° + 63.44° = 116.57°$

$P = |I||V| \cos \phi = \sqrt{5} \; 5 \cos 116.57° = \sqrt{5} \; 5 \, (-0.4472908) = -5$

$P = 5 \, \omega$ the power is positive.

44

EXERCISE 3

1. Calculate the modulus and the argument of the following complex numbers (in the range $-\pi \le \Theta \le \pi$):-

    (i) $Z_1 = 1 + j \sqrt{3}$ (ii) $Z_2 = \sqrt{2} - j$ (iii) $Z_3 = -1 + j \sqrt{3}$

    (iv) $Z_4 = 2 + j$ (v) $Z_5 = -2 + 4j$.

2. Express in polar form the following:-

    (i) $Z_1 = 3 + 4j$ (ii) $Z_2 = 3 - 4j$ (iii) $Z_3 = -3 + 4j$

    (iv) $Z_4 = -3 + 4j$ (v) $Z_5 = \sqrt{2} - j2$.

3. Express in cartesian form the following complex numbers:-

    (i) $Z_1 = 3 \angle -30°$ (ii) $Z_2 = 5 \angle \pi/2$ (iii) $Z_3 = 1 \angle 180°$

    (iv) $Z_4 = 7 \angle -4\pi/3$ (v) $Z_5 = 3 \angle 360°$.

4. Express $Z = \dfrac{1 + 2j}{3 + 4j}$ in the form $x + jy$ and in the form $r \angle \Theta$.

5. A complex number Z has a modulus $\sqrt{2}$ and an argument of $\pi/3$. Write down this complex number in

    (i) the cartesian form
    (ii) the polar form.

6. (a) Mark in Argand diagram the points P_1 and P_2 which represent the two complex number $Z_1 = -1 - j$ and $Z_2 = 1 + j \sqrt{3}$.

    On the same diagram, mark the points P_3 and P_4 which represent $(Z_1 - Z_2)$ and $(Z_1 + Z_2)$ respectively.

    (b) Find the modulus and argument of (i) Z_1 (ii) Z_2 (iii) $Z_1 Z_2$ (iv) Z_1/Z_2 (v) $\dfrac{Z_2}{Z_1}$

7.   If $Z_1 = 5 \underline{/\ 30°}$, $Z_2 = 7 \underline{/\ 50°}$ $Z_3 = 9 \underline{/\ -45°}$.

Determine in polar form the following:-

(i) $Z_1 Z_2 Z_3$ (ii) $Z_1 Z_2$ (iii) $Z_3 Z_1$ (iv) $\dfrac{Z_2}{Z_3}$ (v) $\dfrac{Z_1 Z_2}{Z_3}$

and write down the corresponding cartesian form of the complex numbers.

8.   Find the square roots of the following:-

(i) j (ii) $3 - j4$ (iii) $i - 2$.

9.   The current and voltage in an a.c. circuit are given by $I = 3 + j$ and $V = 5 + j5$. Determine the moduli for I and V and hence find the phase angle between V and I.

If $P = |I|\ |V|\ \cos \Phi$, calculate P.

10.   Find the impedances of the following circuits:-

(i)   If $f = 50$ Hz

Fig. 24

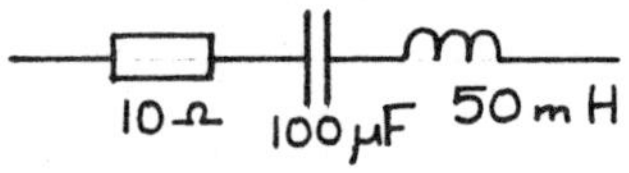

10 Ω   100 μF   50 m H

46

(ii)

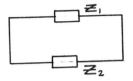

Fig. 25

If $Z_1 = 5 - j8$ and $Z_2 = 10 + j10$ in parallel and hence determine the magnitude of Z and its phase angle.

4. POLAR CO-ORDINATES. SIMPLE CURVE SKETCHING

4. Understands polar co-ordinates.

a. Defines polar coordinates, r and Θ.

b. States the relationships between polar and cartesian coordinates.

c. Converts cartesian to polar coordinates and vice versa.

d. Plots graphs of functions defined in polar coordinates such as $r = a$, $\Theta = \alpha$, $r = k\Theta$, $r = 2a \cos \Theta$.

a. POLAR CO-ORDINATES

A horizontal line is drawn from a fixed point 0 to the right as shown in **Fig 26** The fixed point is called the **pole** and the line to the right of 0 is call the **initial line**.

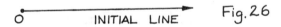
INITIAL LINE Fig. 26

Fig. 26

The initial line is the reference line, which is rotated either clockwise or anti-clockwise, the clockwise angle is negative and the anti-clockwise angle is positive.

A line from the pole 0 is drawn at an angle Θ (positive) to the initial line in an anti-clockwise direction as shown in **Fig 27**.

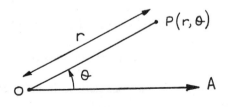

Fig. 27

The magnitude of **OP** = r and in direction to the initial line is θ and therefore, the polar co-ordinates of **P** are (r, Θ). Therefore, the position of a point **P** in a plane is fixed if the distance **OP**, r, and the angle Θ are known.

b. RELATIONSHIP BETWEEN POLAR AND CARTESIAN COORDINATES

The cartesian coordinates may be expressed in terms of r and Θ. (x, y), cartesian coordinates, and (r, Θ), polar coordinates.

The cartesian coordinates of a point **P** is represented by **P** (x, y). The cartesian axes ox and oy intersect perpendicularly at a point 0, alled the origin. The point **P** is plotted as shown in **Fig. 28**, x units horizontally and y units vertically.

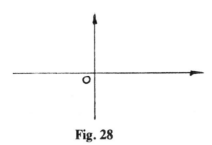

Fig. 28

Let **OP** $= r =$ the radius vector $=$ the magnitude of **OP** and $\Theta =$ the vectorial angle $=$ the direction of **OP** with the **OX** axis (positive). Referring to **Fig. 28**, we have

$$x = r \cos \Theta \qquad \text{and} \qquad y = r \sin \Theta$$

$$r = \sqrt{x^2 + y^2} \qquad \Theta = \tan^{-1} \frac{y}{x}$$

$$(r, \Theta) = \left(\sqrt{x^2 + y^2} \, , \, \tan^{-1} \frac{y}{x} \right).$$

Therefore a curve given cartesian coordinates can be expressed in polar coordinates and vice-versa.

WORKED EXAMPLE 22

Plot the following polar co-ordinate points:

(i) P_1 (1,30°),   (ii) P_2 (2, 60°)

(iii) P_3 (3, π/2)   (iv) P_4 (-2, - π/4)

(v) P_5 (-1, π/2).

SOLUTION 22

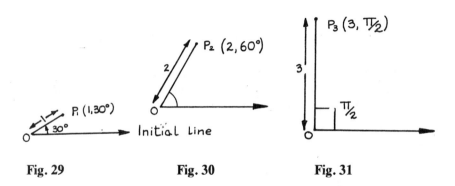

Fig. 29   Fig. 30   Fig. 31

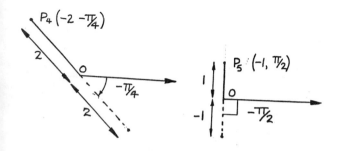

Fig. 32   Fig. 33

SIGN CONVENTIONS

If r is positive in the direction $\mathbf{OP}$ $(r > 0)$, then $\mathbf{OP'}$ $(-r, \theta)$ in the direction θ from the initial line. **Fig. 34** Illustrates this sign convention. A positive value of r is in the direction $\overrightarrow{\mathbf{OP}}$. A negative value r is in the direction $\overrightarrow{\mathbf{PO}}$ produced.

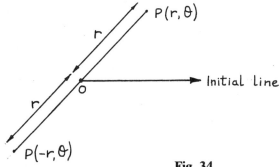

Fig. 34

c. **To convert cartesian to polar co-ordinates**

$$x = r \cos \theta \text{ and } y = r \sin \theta$$

$$\frac{y}{x} = \frac{r \sin \Theta}{r \cos \Theta} = \tan \Theta$$

$$\tan \theta = y/x$$

$$r = \sqrt{x^2 + y^2} \; .$$

WORKED EXAMPLE 23

To convert the following cartesian sets of co-ordinates to the corresponding polar sets of co-ordinates:-

(i) $\left(\dfrac{3}{\sqrt{3}}, \dfrac{3}{\sqrt{2}}\right)$ (ii) $(\sqrt{3}, 1)$ (iii) $(5, 0)$ (iv) $\left(\dfrac{7}{2}, -\dfrac{7\sqrt{3}}{2}\right)$

and V $(3.86, 1.04)$.

SOLUTION 23

(i) $\tan \Theta = y/x = \dfrac{3\sqrt{2}}{3\sqrt{2}} = 1$

and $\Theta = \tan^{-1} 1 \equiv \pi/4$

$$r = \sqrt{x^2 + y^2} = \sqrt{\left(3/\sqrt{2}\right)^2 + \left(3/\sqrt{2}\right)^2} = \sqrt{(9/2) + (9/2)} = \sqrt{9} = 3$$

$r = 3$

therefore $\left(\dfrac{3}{\sqrt{2}}, \dfrac{3}{\sqrt{2}}\right) \equiv \left(3, \dfrac{\pi}{4}\right)$

(ii) $\tan \Theta = y/x = \dfrac{1}{\sqrt{3}}$ and $\Theta = \tan^{-1} \dfrac{1}{\sqrt{3}} = \dfrac{\pi}{6}$

therefore $\left(\sqrt{3}, 1\right) \equiv \left(2, \dfrac{\pi}{6}\right)$

(iii) $\tan \Theta = y/x$ and $\Theta = 0°$ $r = \sqrt{x^2 + y^2} = \sqrt{5^2 + 0^2} = \sqrt{25} = 5$

therefore $(5, 0) \equiv (5, 0°)$.

(iv) $\tan \Theta = y/x = \dfrac{-7\sqrt{3}}{7/2} = \sqrt{3}$ and $\Theta = -\pi/3$.

$$r = \sqrt{x^2 + y^2} = \sqrt{\left(\frac{7}{2}\right)^2 + \left(-7\frac{\sqrt{3}}{2}\right)^2} = \sqrt{\frac{49}{4} + \frac{49+3}{4}} = \sqrt{49}$$

$r = 7$

therefore $\left(\dfrac{7}{2}, \dfrac{-7\sqrt{3}}{2}\right) = (7, -\pi/3).$

(v) $\qquad \tan \Theta = y/x = \dfrac{1.04}{3.86}$

$\qquad = 0.26943$ and $\Theta = 15.079° \approx 15.1°$

$$r = \sqrt{x^2 + y^2} = \sqrt{3.86^2 + 1.04^2} = \sqrt{14.8996 + 1.816}$$

$\qquad = 3.9976 \approx 4.0$ therefore $(3.86, 1.04) \equiv (4, 15.1°).$

TO CONVERT POLAR TO CARTESIAN CO-ORDINATES

$$x = r\cos\theta \ \dots(1)$$
$$y = r\sin\theta \ \dots(2)$$

If r and θ are known, these are substituted in the equations (1) and (2) above and the corresponding cartesian co-ordinates are found.

WORKED EXAMPLE 24

Find the corresponding cartesian co-ordinates to the sets of polar co-ordinates

(i) $(3, \pi/4)$, (ii) $(2, \pi/6)$ (iii) $(5, 0)$ (iv) $(7, -\pi/3)$, (v) $(4, \pi/12)$.

SOLUTION 24

Fig. 35 shows the relationship between polar and cartesian
$\cos \Theta = x/r$ or $x = r \cos \Theta = 3 \cos \pi/4 = \quad 3\sqrt{2}$.
$\sin \Theta = y/r \quad$ or $\quad y = r \sin \Theta = 3 \sin \dfrac{\pi}{4} = 3\sqrt{2}$

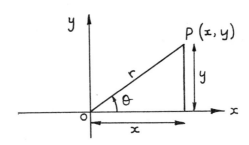

Fig 35

therefore $\left(3, \dfrac{\pi}{4}\right) \equiv \left(\dfrac{3}{\sqrt{2}}, \dfrac{3}{\sqrt{2}}\right).$

(ii) $x = r \cos \Theta = 2 \cos \pi/6 \quad = 2 \dfrac{\sqrt{3}}{2} = \sqrt{3}$

$y = r \sin \theta = 2 \sin \pi/6 = 2 (1/2) = 1$

therefore $\quad (2, \pi/6) \left(\sqrt{3}, 1\right).$

(iii) $x = r \cos \theta = 5 \cos 0 = 5$
$y = r \sin \theta = 5 \sin 0 = 0$

therefore, $(5, 0^c) \equiv (5, 0),$

(iv) $x = r \cos \Theta = 7 \cos (-\pi/3) = 7/2.$
$\quad y = r \sin \Theta\ 7 \sin (-\pi/3) = -7\sqrt{3}/2$

(v) $x = r \cos \theta = 4 \cos \pi/12 = 3.86$
$y = r \sin \theta = 4 \sin \pi/12 = 1.04$

therefore $(4, \pi/12) = (3.86, 1.04).$

Remember that $\quad \sin \pi/4 = \cos \pi/4 = \dfrac{1}{\sqrt{2}} = 0.707$

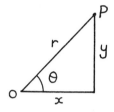

Fig. 36

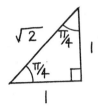

Fig. 37

$$\sin \pi/6 = 1/2$$
$$\cos \pi/6 = \sqrt{3}/2$$

$$\cos 0° = 1$$
$$\sin 0° = 0.$$

$$\sin \ (-\pi/3) = \sqrt{3}/2$$

$$\cos \ (-\pi/3) = 1/2.$$

'Half-lines', the lengths are indefinite but the position of the line is at certain angle, defining the 'half-line'.

Therefore, the graph of $\theta = \alpha$ is a 'half-line' at the particular angle measured clockwise as negative and anti-clockwise as positive.

Graphs of $r = k\theta$

$r = k\Theta$ denotes graphs of 'half-lines' where k is a constant and θ is a variable.

If $k = 1$

Θ°	0	30	60	90	120	150
30°	0	90	180	270	360	450
Θᶜ	0	$\dfrac{\pi}{6}$	$\dfrac{\pi}{3}$	$\dfrac{\pi}{2}$	$\dfrac{2\pi}{3}$	$\dfrac{5\pi}{6}$
$r = \Theta^c$	0	$\dfrac{\pi}{6}$	$\dfrac{\pi}{3}$	$\dfrac{\pi}{2}$	$\dfrac{2\pi}{3}$	$\dfrac{5\pi}{6}$
$r = 2\Theta^c$	0	$\dfrac{\pi}{3}$	$\dfrac{2\pi}{3}$	π	$\dfrac{4\pi}{3}$	$\dfrac{5\pi}{3}$

Θ°	180	210	240	270	300	330	360
30°	540	630	720	810	900	990	1080
Θᶜ	π	$\dfrac{7\pi}{6}$	$\dfrac{4\pi}{3}$	$\dfrac{3\pi}{2}$	$\dfrac{5\pi}{3}$	$\dfrac{11\pi}{6}$	2π
$r = \Theta^c$	π	$\dfrac{7\pi}{6}$	$\dfrac{4\pi}{3}$	$\dfrac{3\pi}{2}$	$\dfrac{5\pi}{3}$	$\dfrac{11\pi}{6}$	2π
$r = 2\,\Theta^c$	2π	$\dfrac{7\pi}{3}$	$\dfrac{8\pi}{3}$	3π	$\dfrac{10\pi}{3}$	$\dfrac{11\pi}{3}$	4π

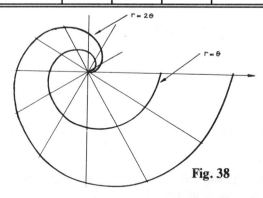

Initial Line

Fig. 38

d.   **Plots graphs of functions defined in polar co-ordinates such as**

$r = a, \theta = , r = k\theta, r = 2a \cos \theta.$

Graph of $r = \alpha$

$r =$ a, the length of r is equal to 'a' for all the angles from 0° to 2π or 360°, that means that the function $r = a$ in polar co-ordinates is a circle with the centre at the pole and radius equal to 'a'.

56

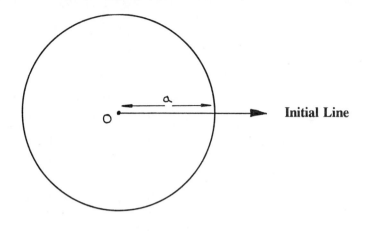

Fig. 39

Graph of θ = α

The polar equation of the initial line is $\theta = 0°$ in radians, or $\theta = 0°$ in degrees.

The polar equations of 'half-lines' are shown in **Fig. 40**

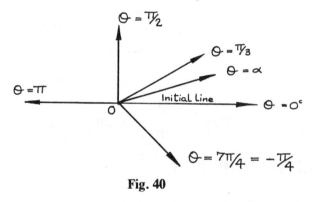

Fig. 40

All the lines drawn from the pole, 0, are drawn at the angles $\theta = 0°$, $\theta = \alpha$, $\theta = \pi/3$, $\theta = \pi/2$ $\theta = 7\pi/4 = -\pi/4$, these are known as half lines.

Graph of $r = 2a \cos \theta$

$\theta°$	0	30	60	90	120
$r = 2a \cos \theta$	$2a$	$1.732a$	a	0	$- a$
$\theta°$	150	180	210	240	270
$r = 2a \cos \theta$	$- 1.732a$	$- 2a$	$- 1.732a$	$- a$	0

$\theta°$	300	330	360
$r = 2a \cos \theta$	a	$1.732a$	$2a$

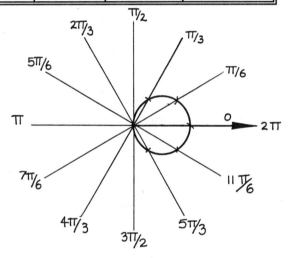

WORKED EXAMPLE 25

Sketch the graphs defined by the polar co-ordinates

(i) $r = 2$ (ii) $\theta = \pi/4$ (iii) $r = 3\theta$ (iv) $r = 2 \cos \theta$
for one revolution.

SOLUTION 25

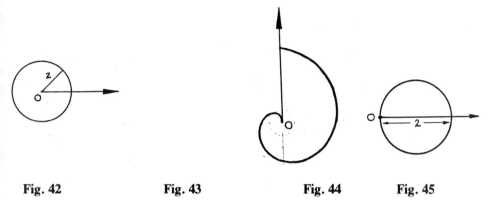

Fig. 42   Fig. 43   Fig. 44   Fig. 45

Polar curve sketching

To sketch the polar curves, it is advisable to tabulate values of Θ in steps of 30° or $\pi/6$ in the range $0 \leq \theta \leq 2\pi$.

If r is a function of $\cos\theta$, the curve is symmetrical about the initial line $\Theta = 0°$ since $\cos(-\Theta) = \cos\Theta$ is an even function, so that values of Θ up to and including π should only be recorded.

In general, the student is advised to think in degrees and work in radians.

EXERCISES 4

1. Plot the following polar co-ordinates:-

    (i)   A $(1, \pi/6)$ (ii) B $(-1, \pi/6)$ (iii) C $(2, \pi/3)$ (iv) D $(-2, \pi/3)$

    (v)   E $(3, -\pi/4)$ (vi) F $(2, 3\pi/4)$ (vii) G $\left(\sqrt{2}, \dfrac{\pi}{8} \right)$

    (viii)   H $(\sqrt{3}, 0^c)$

    (ix)   I $(5, \pi^c)$ J $(-5, \pi/2)$.

2. Plot the following pairs of points and calculate the distances **PQ** in each case.

    (i)   P $(, \pi/6)$, $Q (-1, \pi/6)$

    (ii)   P $(\sqrt{3}, 0^c)$, $Q (-\sqrt{3}, 0^c)$

    (iii)   P $(4, \tan^{-1} 1, Q (4, \tan^{-1} 1)$

3. A triangle ABC has the following polar co-ordinates:

    A $(1,0)$, B $(2, \pi/2)$ and C $(3, \pi)$. Find the area of the **ABC**.

4. Find the polar equations of the following linear cartesian equations:-

    (i) $\dfrac{x}{a} + \dfrac{y}{b} = 1$ (ii) $y = 3x - 5$ (iii) $y = -3x$ (iv) $y = x$.

5. Find the polar equations of the following cartesian curves:-

    (i) $x^2 + y^2 = 1$ (ii) $x^2 + y^2 = 2^2$ (iii) $\dfrac{x^2}{3^2} + \dfrac{y^2}{4^2} = 1$

    (iv) $\dfrac{x^2}{4^2} - \dfrac{y^2}{5^2} = 1$ (v) $yx = 5$ (vi) $y^2 = 4x$ (vii) $x^2 - 4y = 0$

    (viii) $x^2 + y^2 - x - y - 1 = 0$ (ix) $y = \dfrac{1}{x}$.

6.   Find the cartesian equations of the following polar equations:

     (i) $r = 5\theta$ (ii) $r = 3\theta$

     (iii) $r = 2 \cos \theta$ (iv) $\theta = \pi/4$ (v) $\theta = \pi/2$

     (vi) $r = 1$ (vii) $r = 2^2$.

7.   Draw the graphs of the following polar curves:-

     (i) $r = 5$ (ii) $r = 3\theta$ (iii) $r = 3 \cos \theta$ (iv) $\theta = \pi/3$ (v) $\theta = -\pi/2$.

8.   Why do we need the polar co-ordinate system? Illustrate your answer by considering an example in the cartesian co-ordinate system and an example in the polar co-ordinate system.

5. MATRICES AND DETERMINANTS

Understands the notation of matrices and determinants.

a.   Recognises the notation for a matrix.

b.   Calculates the sum and difference of two matrices (2 x 2 only).

c.   Calculates the product of two matrices (2 x 2 only).

d.   Demonstrates that the product of two matrices is, in general, non-commutative.

e.   Defines the unit matrix.

f.   Recognises the notation for a determinant.

g.   Evaluates a 2 x 2 determinant.

a.   NOTATION OF A MATRIX

What is a matrix?

A matrix is an array of numbers enclosed by two brackets, such as the following examples:-

(i) $\begin{pmatrix} 2 & 3 \\ 1 & -2 \end{pmatrix}$ (ii) $\begin{pmatrix} 1 \\ 2 \end{pmatrix}$ (iii) $(2 \ -3)$.

(iv) $\begin{pmatrix} 1 & 2 & 3 \\ -1 & 2 & 4 \end{pmatrix}$ (v) $\begin{pmatrix} 1 & 2 \\ 3 & 4 \\ 5 & 6 \end{pmatrix}$ (vi) $\begin{pmatrix} 1 & 2 & 3 \\ 4 & 5 & 6 \\ 7 & 8 & 9 \end{pmatrix}$

Each number is called an **element** of the matrix, the number of elements in (i) are four, in (ii) are two, in (iii) are two, in (iv) are six, in (v) are six, in (v) are nine, in the above examples there are **rows** and **columns**.

(i)   has two rows and two columns

(ii)   has two rows and one column

(iii) has one row and two columns

(iv)   has two rows and three columns

(v)   has three rows and two columns and

(vi)   has three rows and three columns.

The **order** of the matrix is denoted as follows:-

For (i) 2 x 2 the first two denotes the rows and the second two denotes the columns.

For (ii) 2 x 1 two   rows x one   column
For (iii) 1 x 2 one   row x two   columns
For (iv) 2 x 3 two   rows x three columns
For (v) 3 x 2 three rows x two   columns
For (vi) 3 x 3 three rows x three columns.

Types of matrices

EXAMPLE   (i)   is a **square matrix**
(ii)   is a **column matrix**
(iii) is a **row matrix**
(iv)   is a **rectangular matrix**
(v)   is a **rectangular matrix**
(vi)   is a **square matrix** or a 3 **square matrix**.

In a square matrix like the last example, 1, 5, 9 are called its **diagonal elements**. The sum of the diagonal elements of a square matrix of example (vi) is called the **trace** of the matrix, that is, $1 + 5 + 9 = 15$ is the trace of the matrix.

Zero or Null Matrix

$$\begin{pmatrix} 0 & 0 \\ & \\ 0 & 0 \end{pmatrix} \qquad \text{and} \qquad \begin{pmatrix} 0 & 0 & 0 \\ 0 & 0 & 0 \\ 0 & 0 & 0 \end{pmatrix}$$

are null matrices of order two and three respectively.

Diagonal matrix

The matrix is a square matrix in which all the elements are zero except the diagonal elements.

$$\begin{pmatrix} 1 & 0 \\ & \\ 0 & 2 \end{pmatrix} \qquad \text{and} \qquad \begin{pmatrix} 1 & 0 & 0 \\ 0 & 2 & 0 \\ 0 & 0 & 3 \end{pmatrix}$$

are diagonal matrices of order two and three respectively.   Note that a diagnal matrix runs from upper left to lower right.

Unit Matrix

This is a diagonal matrix where all the diagonal elements are unity such as

$$I = \begin{pmatrix} 1 & 0 \\ & \\ 0 & 1 \end{pmatrix} \qquad I = \begin{pmatrix} 1 & 0 & 0 \\ 0 & 1 & 0 \\ 0 & 0 & 1 \end{pmatrix}$$

of order two and three respectively. The unit matrix is denoted by the letter I.

Matrices are in general denoted by capital letters such as A, B, C.

b.   **TO CALCULATE THE SUM AND DIFFERENCE OF TWO MATRICES (2 x 2 only)**

          ADDITION OF MATRICES

$$A = \begin{pmatrix} a_{11} & a_{12} \\ a_{21} & a_{22} \end{pmatrix}$$

where A denotes the 2 x 2 matrix with elements a_{11}, a_{12}, a_{21} and a_{22}. This is a general form of a 2 x 2 matrix. The subscripts denote the position of the elements. for example a_{11}, the first subscript 1 denotes the first row and the second subscript 1 denotes the first column, a_{12}, the first subscript 1 denotes the first row and the second subscript 2 denotes the second column. Generally, the first subscript denotes the row and the second subscript denotes the column.

If $B = \begin{pmatrix} b_{11} & b_{12} \\ b_{21} & b_{22} \end{pmatrix}$ and $A = \begin{pmatrix} a_{11} & a_{12} \\ a_{21} & a_{22} \end{pmatrix}$ then

$$A + B = \begin{pmatrix} a_1 & a_{12} \\ a_{21} & a_{22} \end{pmatrix} + \begin{pmatrix} b_{11} & b_{12} \\ b_{21} & b_{22} \end{pmatrix}$$

$$B + A = \begin{pmatrix} b_{11} & b_{12} \\ b_{21} & b_{22} \end{pmatrix} + \begin{pmatrix} a_{11} & a_{12} \\ a_{21} & a_{22} \end{pmatrix}$$

$$= \begin{pmatrix} b_{11} + a_{11} & b_{12} + a_{12} \\ b_{21} + a_{21} & b_{22} + a_{22} \end{pmatrix}.$$

Therefore, from the above $A + B = B + A$ and the addition of matrices is associative.

WORKED EXAMPLE 26

Find the sums of the following:-

(i) $A + B$ (ii) $B + A$ (iii) $A + C$ (iv) $B + C$.

$$\text{If } A = \begin{pmatrix} -1 & 2 \\ 3 & -1 \end{pmatrix}, \quad B = \begin{pmatrix} 3 & -4 \\ 2 & 1 \end{pmatrix}, \quad C = \begin{pmatrix} 0 & -1 \\ -1 & 2 \end{pmatrix}$$

SOLUTION 26

(i) $A + B = \begin{pmatrix} -1 & 2 \\ 3 & -1 \end{pmatrix} + \begin{pmatrix} 3 & -4 \\ 2 & 1 \end{pmatrix} = \begin{pmatrix} -1 + 3 & 2 - 4 \\ 3 + 2 & -1 + 1 \end{pmatrix}$

$$= \begin{pmatrix} 2 & -2 \\ 5 & 0 \end{pmatrix}$$

(ii) $B + A = \begin{pmatrix} 3 & -4 \\ 2 & 1 \end{pmatrix} + \begin{pmatrix} -1 & 2 \\ 3 & -1 \end{pmatrix}$

66

$$= \begin{pmatrix} 3 - 1 & -4 + 2 \\ 2 + 3 & 1 - 1 \end{pmatrix} = \begin{pmatrix} 2 & -2 \\ 5 & 0 \end{pmatrix}$$

note that **A + B = B + A**.

(iii) $A + C = \begin{pmatrix} -1 & 2 \\ 3 & -1 \end{pmatrix} + \begin{pmatrix} 0 & -1 \\ -1 & 2 \end{pmatrix} = \begin{pmatrix} -1 + 0 & 2 - 1 \\ 3 - 1 & -1 + 2 \end{pmatrix}$

$$= \begin{pmatrix} -1 & 1 \\ 2 & 1 \end{pmatrix}$$

(iv) $B + C = \begin{pmatrix} 3 & -4 \\ 2 & 1 \end{pmatrix} + \begin{pmatrix} 0 & -1 \\ -1 & 2 \end{pmatrix} = \begin{pmatrix} 3 + 0 & -4 - 1 \\ 2 - 11 & 1 + 2 \end{pmatrix}$

SUBTRACTION OF MATRICES

$$A - B = \begin{pmatrix} a_{11} & a_{12} \\ a_{21} & a_{22} \end{pmatrix} - \begin{pmatrix} b_{11} & b_{12} \\ b_{21} & b_{22} \end{pmatrix}$$

$$= \begin{pmatrix} a_{11} - b_{11} & a_{12} - b_{12} \\ a_{21} - b_{21} & a_{22} - b_{22} \end{pmatrix}$$

$$B - A = \begin{pmatrix} b_{11} - a_{11} & b_{12} - a_{12} \\ b_{21} - a_{21} & b_{22} - a_{22} \end{pmatrix}$$

We can see that the substraction is similar to the addition, the corresponding elements are either substracted or added.

WORKED EXAMPLE 27

If $A = \begin{pmatrix} 1 & -1 \\ 0 & 0 \end{pmatrix}$ $\quad B = \begin{pmatrix} 2 & 3 \\ -1 & -1 \end{pmatrix}$ $\quad C = \begin{pmatrix} 1 & 1 \\ 1 & 0 \end{pmatrix}$

Find (i) **A - B** (ii) **A - C** (iii) **C - B.**

SOLUTION 27

$$A - B = \begin{pmatrix} 1 & -1 \\ 0 & 0 \end{pmatrix} - \begin{pmatrix} 2 & 3 \\ -1 & -1 \end{pmatrix} = \begin{pmatrix} 1-2 & -1-3 \\ 0-(-1) & 0-(-1) \end{pmatrix}$$

$$= \begin{pmatrix} -1 & -4 \\ 1 & 1 \end{pmatrix}$$

$$A - C = \begin{pmatrix} 1 & -1 \\ 0 & 0 \end{pmatrix} - \begin{pmatrix} 1 & 1 \\ 1 & 0 \end{pmatrix} = \begin{pmatrix} 1-1 & -1-1 \\ 0-1 & 0-0 \end{pmatrix}$$

$$= \begin{pmatrix} 0 & -2 \\ -1 & 0 \end{pmatrix}$$

$$C - B = \begin{pmatrix} 1 & 1 \\ 1 & 0 \end{pmatrix} - \begin{pmatrix} 2 & 3 \\ -1 & -1 \end{pmatrix} = \begin{pmatrix} 1-2 & 1-3 \\ 1-(-1) & 0-(-1) \end{pmatrix} = \begin{pmatrix} -1 & -2 \\ 2 & 1 \end{pmatrix}$$

What is the meaning of 2**A** if $A = \begin{pmatrix} 1 & 2 \\ 3 & 4 \end{pmatrix}$?

It means that each element is multiplied by 2.

$$2A = 2\begin{pmatrix} 1 & 2 \\ 3 & 4 \end{pmatrix} = \begin{pmatrix} 2 & 4 \\ 6 & 8 \end{pmatrix}$$

WORKED EXAMPLE 28

If $A = \begin{pmatrix} 1 & 0 \\ 1 & -1 \end{pmatrix}$ $B = \begin{pmatrix} -3 & 5 \\ 2 & -1 \end{pmatrix}$

Find (i) 3 **A** + **B**   (ii)   4**B** - 2**A**

SOLUTION 28

(i) $3A + B = 3\begin{pmatrix} 1 & 0 \\ 1 & -1 \end{pmatrix} + \begin{pmatrix} -3 & 5 \\ 2 & -1 \end{pmatrix} = \begin{pmatrix} 3 & 0 \\ 3 & -3 \end{pmatrix} + \begin{pmatrix} -3 & 5 \\ 2 & -1 \end{pmatrix}$

$$= \begin{pmatrix} 3-3 & 0+5 \\ 3+2 & -3-1 \end{pmatrix} = \begin{pmatrix} 0 & 5 \\ 5 & -4 \end{pmatrix}$$

(ii)

$$4B - 2A = 4 \begin{pmatrix} -3 & 5 \\ 2 & -1 \end{pmatrix} - 2 \begin{pmatrix} 1 & 0 \\ 1- & 1 \end{pmatrix}$$

$$= \begin{pmatrix} -12 & 20 \\ 8 & -4 \end{pmatrix} - \begin{pmatrix} 2 & 0 \\ 2 & -2 \end{pmatrix}$$

$$= \begin{pmatrix} -12 & -2 & 20 & -0 \\ 8 & -2 & -4- & (-2) \end{pmatrix} = \begin{pmatrix} -14 & 20 \\ 6 & -2 \end{pmatrix}.$$

C. CALCULATE THE PRODUCT OF TWO MATRICES (2 X 2) ONLY.

$$\text{If } A = \begin{pmatrix} a_{11} & a_{12} \end{pmatrix} \qquad B = \begin{pmatrix} b_{11} & b_{12} \\ b_{21} & b_{22} \end{pmatrix}.$$

$$A B = \begin{pmatrix} a_{11} & a_{12} \\ a_{22} & a_{22} \end{pmatrix} \begin{pmatrix} b_{11} & b_{12} \\ \downarrow b_{21} & b_{22} \end{pmatrix}$$

To find the product of two matrices, the technique is different, the arrows shown above help a great deal, the result is

$$A B = \begin{pmatrix} a_{11} \ b_{11} + b_{12} \ b_{21} & a_{11} \ b_{12} + a_{12} \ b_{22} \\ a_{21} \ b_{11} + a_{22} \ b_{21} & a_{21} \ b_{12} + a_{22} \ b_{22} \end{pmatrix}$$

Observe that the elements of the tails of the arrows are multiplied and added to the product of the elements of the arrow heads.

Repeat for practice.

$$BA = \begin{pmatrix} b_{11} & b_{12} \\ \\ b_{21} & b_{22} \end{pmatrix} \overset{\rightarrow}{\begin{pmatrix} a_{11} & a_{12} \\ \\ \downarrow a_{21} & a_{22} \end{pmatrix}}$$

$$= \begin{pmatrix} a_{11} & a_{11} + b_{12} & a_{21} & b_{11} & a_{12} + b_{12} & a_{22} \\ \\ b_{21} & a_{11} + b_{22} & a_{21} & b_{21} & a_{12} + b_{22} & a_{22} \end{pmatrix}.$$

WORKED EXAMPLE 29

If $\quad A = \begin{pmatrix} -1 & 2 \\ \\ -2 & -3 \end{pmatrix}$ and $\qquad B = \begin{pmatrix} 1 & 2 \\ \\ 3 & 4 \end{pmatrix}$

Find (i) $A\,B$ (ii) $B\,A$

SOLUTION 29

(i)

$$AB = \begin{pmatrix} -1 & 2 \\ \\ -2 & -3 \end{pmatrix} \begin{pmatrix} 1 & 2 \\ \\ 3 & 4 \end{pmatrix} = \begin{pmatrix} (-1)(1) + (2)(3) & (-1)(2) + (2)(4) \\ \\ (-2)(1) + (-3)(3) & (-2)(2) + (-3)(4) \end{pmatrix}$$

$$= \begin{pmatrix} -1 + 6 & -2 + 8 \\ \\ -2 - 9 & -4 - 12 \end{pmatrix} = \begin{pmatrix} 5 & 6 \\ \\ -11 & -16 \end{pmatrix}$$

(ii)

$$B\,A = \begin{pmatrix} 1 & 2 \\ \\ 3 & 4 \end{pmatrix} \begin{pmatrix} -1 & 2 \\ \\ -2 & -3 \end{pmatrix}$$

$$BA = \begin{pmatrix} 1 & 2 \\ 3 & 4 \end{pmatrix} \begin{pmatrix} -1 & 2 \\ -2 & -3 \end{pmatrix}$$

$$= \begin{pmatrix} (1)(-1) + (2)(-2) & (1)(2) - (2)(3) \\ (3)(-1) + (4)(-2) & (3)(2) + (4)(-3) \end{pmatrix}$$

$$= \begin{pmatrix} -1-4 & 2-6 \\ -3-8 & 6-12 \end{pmatrix} = \begin{pmatrix} -5 & -4 \\ -11 & -6 \end{pmatrix}$$

Note that **A B** is not equal to **B A**

$$AB \ne BA$$

WORKED EXAMPLE 30

$$A = \begin{pmatrix} 3 & 7 \\ 5 & -6 \end{pmatrix}, \quad B = \begin{pmatrix} 1 & 0 \\ 0 & 1 \end{pmatrix}, \quad C = \begin{pmatrix} 0 & 0 \\ 0 & 0 \end{pmatrix}$$

Find (i) **A B**   (ii) **B A**   (iii) **A C**   (iv) **C B**

SOLUTION 30

(i)
$$AB = \begin{pmatrix} 3 & 7 \\ 5 & -6 \end{pmatrix} \begin{pmatrix} 1 & 0 \\ 0 & 1 \end{pmatrix} = \begin{pmatrix} 3 \times 1 + 3 \times 0 & 7 \times 0 + 7 \times 1 \\ 5 \times 1 + (-6) \times 0 & 5 \times 0 + (-6)(1) \end{pmatrix}$$

$$= \begin{pmatrix} 3 & 7 \\ 5 & -6 \end{pmatrix}$$

Note that $AB = A$.

(ii) $BA = \begin{pmatrix} 1 & 0 \\ 0 & 1 \end{pmatrix}\begin{pmatrix} 3 & 7 \\ 5 & -6 \end{pmatrix} = \begin{pmatrix} 1 \times 3 + 0 \times 5 & 1 \times 7 + 0(-6) \\ 0 \times 3 + 1 \times 5 & 0 \times 7 + 1(-6) \end{pmatrix}$

$= \begin{pmatrix} 3 & 7 \\ 5 & -6 \end{pmatrix}$

Note that $BA = A$.

(iii)

$A\,C = \begin{pmatrix} 3 & 7 \\ 5 & -6 \end{pmatrix}\begin{pmatrix} 0 & 0 \\ 0 & 0 \end{pmatrix} = \begin{pmatrix} 3 \times 0 + 7 \times 0 & 3 \times 0 + 7 \times 0 \\ 5 \times 0 + (-6) \times 0 & 5 \times 0 + (-6) \times 0 \end{pmatrix}$

$= \begin{pmatrix} 0 & 0 \\ 0 & 0 \end{pmatrix}$

Note $AC = C$.

(iv)

$C\,B = \begin{pmatrix} 0 & 0 \\ 0 & 0 \end{pmatrix}\begin{pmatrix} 1 & 0 \\ 0 & 0 \end{pmatrix} = \begin{pmatrix} 0 \times 1 + 0 \times 1 & 0 \times 0 + 0 \times 1 \\ 0 \times 1 + 0 \times 0 & 0 \times 0 + 0 \times 1 \end{pmatrix}$

$= \begin{pmatrix} 0 & 0 \\ 0 & 0 \end{pmatrix}$

Note $CB = C$.

d. Demonstrates that the product of two matrices is in general, non-commutative.

We have already demonstrated that **AB** is not equal to **BA**, that is,

$$\textbf{AB} \ne \textbf{BA}.$$

If $\quad A = \begin{pmatrix} 1 & 2 \\ -2 & -1 \end{pmatrix} \quad$ and $\quad B = \begin{pmatrix} 2 & 3 \\ 1 & 1 \end{pmatrix}$

$$AB = \begin{pmatrix} 1 & 2 \\ -2 & -1 \end{pmatrix}\begin{pmatrix} 2 & 3 \\ \downarrow 1 & 1 \end{pmatrix} = \begin{pmatrix} 1 \times 2 + 2 \times 1 & 1 \times 3 + 2 \times 1 \\ (-2) \times 2 + (-1)(1) & (-2)(3) + (-1)(1) \end{pmatrix}$$

$$= \begin{pmatrix} 4 & 5 \\ -5 & -7 \end{pmatrix}$$

$$BA = \begin{pmatrix} 2 & 3 \\ 1 & 1 \end{pmatrix}\begin{pmatrix} 1 & 2 \\ \downarrow -2 & -1 \end{pmatrix} = \begin{pmatrix} 2 \times 1 + 3 \,(-2) & 2 \times 2 + 3\,(-1) \\ 1 \times 1 + 1 \times (-2) & 1 \times 2 + (1)\,(-1) \end{pmatrix}$$

$$= \begin{pmatrix} -4 & 1 \\ -1 & 1 \end{pmatrix}$$

therefore **AB** $\ne$ **BA** and the product of two matrices is, in general, non commutative.

But we have seen that if **B** is a unit matrix and **A** is a matrix of different elements then **AB** = **A** and **BA** = **A**, in this case **AB** = **BA**.

e. Defines the unit matrix

A unit matrix is a matrix whose diagonal elements are equal to 1

$$I = \begin{pmatrix} 1 & 0 \\ 0 & 1 \end{pmatrix}$$

Any matrix that is pre- or post-multiplied by **I** is unaltered.

AI = **I**, **A** is post multiplied by **I**, **IA** = **I**, **A** is pre-multiplied, **AI** = **IA** = **A**.

f. Recognises the notation for a determinant

A determinant is an array of elements enclosed by vertical lines such that

$$\begin{vmatrix} a & b \\ c & d \end{vmatrix}$$

and means that $ad - cb$

therefore
$$\begin{vmatrix} a & b \\ c & d \end{vmatrix} = ad - bc$$

The number of rows is equal to the number of columns, 2 x 2 or 3 x 3 or 4 x 4, but we will restrict our work to 2 x 2.

a, b, c, d are called the elements of the determinant.

8. Evaluates a 2 x 2 determinant

WORKED EXAMPLE 30

Evaluate the following determinants:

(i)
$$\begin{vmatrix} a & b \\ c & d \end{vmatrix}$$

(ii)
$$\begin{vmatrix} -1 & -1 \\ -1 & -1 \end{vmatrix}$$

(iii)
$$\begin{vmatrix} 1 & 2 \\ 3 & 4 \end{vmatrix}$$

SOLUTION 31

(i)
$$\begin{vmatrix} a & b \\ c & d \end{vmatrix} = ad - cd$$

(ii)
$$\begin{vmatrix} -1 & -1 \\ -1 & -1 \end{vmatrix} = (-1)(-1) - (-1)(-1) = 1 - 1 = 0$$

(iii)
$$\begin{vmatrix} 1 & 2 \\ 3 & 4 \end{vmatrix} = 1 \times 4 - 3 \times 2 = 4 - 6 = -2$$

It is observed that if the rows are the same or if the columns are the same as in example (ii) the determinant is equal to zero.

WORKED EXAMPLE 32

Factorise
$$\begin{vmatrix} a & 1 \\ a^2 & 1 \end{vmatrix}$$

SOLUTION 32

$$\begin{vmatrix} a & 1 \\ a^2 & 1 \end{vmatrix} = a \begin{vmatrix} 1 & 1 \\ a & 1 \end{vmatrix} = a \, \Delta$$

If $a = 1$ then $= \Delta = \begin{vmatrix} 1 & 1 \\ 1 & 1 \end{vmatrix} = 0$ and $a - 1$ is a factor
or $1 - a$ is a factor

therefore
$$= a \, (1 - a) = a - a^2$$

$$\begin{vmatrix} a & 1 \\ a^2 & 1 \end{vmatrix} = a \begin{vmatrix} 1 & 1 \\ a & 1 \end{vmatrix} = a \, (a - 1)$$

EXERCISES 5

1.   Write down the following matrices:

    (i)   a 2 x 2 unit matrix   (ii)   a 2 x 2 zero matrix

    (iii)   a 2 x 2 diagonal matrix.

2.   Write down the following matrices:

    (i)   a 3 x 1 matrix   (i)   a 3 x 3 square matrix

    (iii)   a 1 x 3 row matrix   (iv)   a 3 x 2 or 2 x 3 rectangular matrix

    (v)   a 3 x 3 unit matrix

    (iv)   a 3 x 3 diagnonal matrix (vii)   a null 3 x 3 matrix

3.   If $A = \begin{pmatrix} -1 & 2 \\ -3 & 3 \end{pmatrix}$, $B = \begin{pmatrix} 1 & -2 \\ 3 & 5 \end{pmatrix}$, $C = \begin{pmatrix} 0 & 1 \\ 1 & 0 \end{pmatrix}$.

Find (i) $A + B + C$ (ii) $2A - 3C + 2B$, (iii) $5B + 4A$

4.   If $A = \begin{pmatrix} 6 & 7 \\ 8 & 9 \end{pmatrix}$ $B = \begin{pmatrix} 10 & 11 \\ 12 & 13 \end{pmatrix}$ $C = \begin{pmatrix} 0 & 1 \\ -1 & 0 \end{pmatrix}$.

Find (i) ABC (ii) A^2 (iii) BC (iv) AC (v) CB.

5.   Show that $AB \neq BA$ and $BC \neq CB$ if A, B, C are the matrices shown in exercise 4.

6.   Are matrices associative or commutative?

Give a simple example in each case to illustrate the associativity and communtativity.

7. What is a unit matrix and what is the effect of multiplying a matrix by unit matrix? Illustrate the answers with examples.

8. A column vector $\begin{pmatrix} x \\ y \end{pmatrix}$ is a column matrix $\begin{pmatrix} x \\ y \end{pmatrix}$.

If $O\,P = \begin{pmatrix} 3 \\ 5 \end{pmatrix}$ and $O\,Q = \begin{pmatrix} 2 \\ 7 \end{pmatrix}$

find the resultant of these two vectors by adding the ordered pairs vectorially and by adding the two matrices and verify that they are the same.

9. If $A = \begin{pmatrix} 1 & b \\ a & 0 \end{pmatrix}$, $B = \begin{pmatrix} -1 & 2 \\ 3 & 4 \end{pmatrix}$, $C = \begin{pmatrix} 5 & 10 \\ -1 & 2 \end{pmatrix}$

Determine the values of a and b if $AB = C$.

Explain the equality of a matrix.

10. Evaluate the determinants:

(i) $\begin{vmatrix} a & b \\ a^2 & b^2 \end{vmatrix}$ (ii) $\begin{vmatrix} 1 & 3 \\ 2 & 4 \end{vmatrix}$ (iii) $\begin{vmatrix} a & 3 \\ 4 & a \end{vmatrix}$

11. If the determinants are equal to zero, find the value of a, without evaluating

(i) $\begin{vmatrix} a & 2 \\ a^2 & 4 \end{vmatrix}$ (ii) $\begin{vmatrix} 3 & a \\ 9 & a^2 \end{vmatrix}$ (iii) $\begin{vmatrix} 1 & a \\ a & 1 \end{vmatrix}$

12. Factorise the determinants:

(i) $\begin{vmatrix} 2x & 1 \\ 8x^2 & 2 \end{vmatrix}$ (ii) $\begin{vmatrix} 2y & x \\ 4y^2 & x^2 \end{vmatrix}$.

6. SOLUTIONS OF SIMULTANEOUS EQUATIONS

Solves simultaneous equations with two unknowns using matrices and determinants.

a. Solves simultaneous linear equations with two unknowns using determinants.

b. Describes the meaning of a determinant whose value is zero, and defines a singular matrix.

c. Obtains the inverse of a 2 x 2 matrix.

d. Solves simultaneous linear equations with two unknowns by means of matrices.

e. Relates the use of matrices to simple technical problems.

LINEAR SIMULTANEOUS EQUATIONS WITH TWO UNKNOWNS

Solve first of all the linear simultaneous equations using an algebraic method

$$3x - y = 9 \quad \dots(1)$$

$$-4x + 3y = 7 \quad \dots(2)$$

Multiply each term of equation (1) by 3

$$9x - 3y = 27$$

$$-4x + 3y = 7$$

adding these equations we have

$$5x = 20$$

$$x = 4$$

substituting $x = 4$ in equation (1)

$$3(4) - y = 9$$

$$12 - 9 = y$$

$$y = 3$$

therefore, using the elimination and substitution methods, we have found that the above equations are simultaneously verified by putting
$x = 4$ and $y = 3$. The procedure shall be more complicated if we had to solve three unknowns or even more.

We are going to restrict ourselves to two unknowns and solve these equations by determinants and by matrices.

a. **To solve simultaneous linear equations with two unknowns using determinants.**

$$3x - y = 9$$

$$-4x + 3y = -7$$

Rewrite

$$3x - y - 9 = 0$$

$$-4x + 3y + 7 = 0$$

The array of numbers are

$$\begin{array}{ccc} 3 & -1 & -9 \\ -4 & 3 & 7 \end{array}$$

We can form three determinants Δ_1, Δ_2, and Δ where

$$\Delta = \begin{vmatrix} 3 & -1 \\ -4 & 3 \end{vmatrix} \quad \Delta_1 = \begin{vmatrix} -1 & -9 \\ 3 & 7 \end{vmatrix} \quad \Delta_2 = \begin{vmatrix} 3 & -9 \\ -4 & 7 \end{vmatrix}.$$

Observe that in order to write , we delete the column of the constants, in order to write $_1$ we delete the column, of the coefficients of x and in order to write $_2$, we delete the columns of the coefficients of y.

Crammer's rule states:

$$\frac{x}{\Delta_1} = -\frac{y}{\Delta_2} = \frac{1}{\Delta}$$

$$x = \frac{\Delta_1}{\Delta} \qquad \text{and} \qquad y = -\frac{\Delta_2}{\Delta}$$

$$\Delta_1 = \begin{vmatrix} -1 & -9 \\ 3 & 7 \end{vmatrix} = (-1)(7) - (3)(-9) = -7 + 27 = 20$$

$$\Delta_2 = \begin{vmatrix} 3 & -9 \\ -4 & 7 \end{vmatrix} = (3)(7) - (-4)(-9) = 21 - 36 = --15$$

$$\Delta = \begin{vmatrix} 3 & -1 \\ -4 & 3 \end{vmatrix} = (3)(3) - (-1)(-4) = 9 - 4 = 5$$

therefore $x = \dfrac{\Delta_1}{\Delta} = \dfrac{20}{5} = 4$

$y = -\dfrac{\Delta_2}{\Delta} = -\dfrac{(-15)}{5} = 3$

and the answers are the same as before but with a different method.

The use of determinants may be more tedious, but is a systematic method which can be adopted in solving any number of unknowns, it is a computer orientated method.

b.   **Describes the meaning of a determinant whose value is zero, and defines a singular matrix.**

A singular matrix is a matrix whose determinant is zero.

If $M = \begin{pmatrix} a_{11} & a_{12} \\ a_{21} & a_{22} \end{pmatrix}$ then $|M| = 0$

83

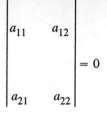

$$\begin{vmatrix} a_{11} & a_{12} \\ a_{21} & a_{22} \end{vmatrix} = 0$$

$$a_{11}\ a_{22} - a_{21}\ a_{12} = 0$$

We have seen that when two rows or two columns of a determinant are the same, then the determinant is zero.

If the determinant is zero, then the solutions are not defined and therefore there are no solution.

c.   **Obtains the inverse of 2 x 2 matrix**

THE INVERSE OF A MATRIX

We have seen how to add, to substract and to multiply matrices, now we have to show how to divide two matrices.

NOTATION OF THE INVERSE MATRIX

The inverse of a matrix **A** is denoted as A^{-1}

TO FIND THE INVERSE MATRIX OF A

Step I $A^* = A$ star (read as)
         A^* denotes the cofactors of the elements of the matrix **A**.

If $A = \begin{pmatrix} a_{11} & a_{12} \\ a_{21} & a_{22} \end{pmatrix}$ the elements are a_{11}, a_{12}, a_{21} and a_{22}.

The minor of the element a_{11} is found by deleting the new row containing a_{11} and deleting the column containing a_{11} thus the minor of a_{11} is a_{22}.

$$a_{11} \quad a_{12}$$

$$a_{21} \quad a_{22}$$

The minor of a_{12} is a_{21} since

$$a_{11} \quad a_{12}$$

$$a_{21} \quad a_{22}$$

The minor of a_{21} is a_{12} since

$$a_{11} \quad a_{12}$$

$$a_{21} \quad a_{22}$$

and the minor of a_{22} is a_{11} since

$$a_{11} \quad a_{12}$$

$$a_{21} \quad a_{22}$$

The minors of **A** are $\begin{pmatrix} a_{22} & a_{21} \\ a_{12} & a_{11} \end{pmatrix}$

The cofactor of **A** are found by writing plus and minus alternatively starting with a plus at the upper left.

Therefore $\quad A^* = \begin{pmatrix} a_{22} & -a_{21} \\ -a_{12} & a_{11} \end{pmatrix}$

WORKED EXAMPLE 33

If $M = \begin{pmatrix} 1 & -2 \\ 3 & -4 \end{pmatrix}$ find the M^*

SOLUTION 33

$M^* = \begin{pmatrix} -4 & -3 \\ 2 & 1 \end{pmatrix}$

Step II A^{*T} Transpose of A^* that is the columns are written as rows and the rows as columns.

$$A^{*\underline{T}} = \begin{pmatrix} a_{22} & -a_{12} \\ -a_{21} & a_{11} \end{pmatrix}$$

A^{*T} is called the adjoint matrix of A

Step III Finally to obtain the inverse matrix of A, we divide the adjoint matrix of A by the determinant of A.

$$A^{-1} = \frac{A^{*\underline{T}}}{|A|}$$

WORKED EXAMPLE 34

Find the inverse matrix of the $A = \begin{pmatrix} 3 & -1 \\ -4 & 3 \end{pmatrix}$.

86

SOLUTION 34

STEP I

The minors of $\mathbf{A} = \begin{pmatrix} 3 & -4 \\ -1 & 3 \end{pmatrix}$

The cofactors of $A = A^* = \begin{pmatrix} 3 & 4 \\ 1 & 3 \end{pmatrix}$

STEP II

$$A = A^{*T} = \begin{pmatrix} 3 & 1 \\ 4 & 3 \end{pmatrix}$$

The adjoint matrix of

STEP III

$$A^{-1} = \frac{A^{*T}}{|A|}$$

$$|A| = \begin{vmatrix} 3 & -4 \\ -1 & 3 \end{vmatrix} = 3 \times 3 - 1 \times 4 = 9 - 4 = 5$$

$$A^1 = \frac{\begin{pmatrix} 3 & 1 \\ 4 & 3 \end{pmatrix}}{5} = \begin{pmatrix} \dfrac{3}{5} & \dfrac{1}{5} \\ \dfrac{4}{5} & \dfrac{3}{5} \end{pmatrix}$$

WORKED EXAMPLE 35

If $A = \begin{pmatrix} 3 & -1 \\ -4 & 3 \end{pmatrix}$ and $B = \begin{pmatrix} \dfrac{3}{5} & \dfrac{1}{5} \\ \dfrac{4}{5} & \dfrac{3}{5} \end{pmatrix}$

Find **AB**

SOLUTION 35

$$A B = \begin{pmatrix} 3 & -1 \\ -4 & 3 \end{pmatrix} \begin{pmatrix} \dfrac{3}{5} & \dfrac{1}{5} \\ \dfrac{4}{5} & \dfrac{3}{5} \end{pmatrix}$$

$$= \begin{pmatrix} \dfrac{9}{5} - \dfrac{4}{5} & \dfrac{3}{5} - \dfrac{3}{5} \\ -\dfrac{12}{5} + \dfrac{12}{5} & -\dfrac{4}{5} + \dfrac{9}{5} \end{pmatrix} = \begin{pmatrix} 1 & 0 \\ 0 & \end{pmatrix}$$

$$A B = \begin{pmatrix} 1 & 0 \\ 0 & 1 \end{pmatrix} = I = \text{unit matrix.}$$

The use of finding the inverse matrix is to multiply the matrix **A** by its inverse and find that $(A A^1 = I)$ it is equal to unit matrix.

d.   **Solves simultaneous linear equations with two unknowns by means of matrices.**

Solve $3x - y = 9$

$$-4x + 3y = 7$$

by means of matrices

1

In matrix form these two equations may be written as

$$\begin{pmatrix} 3 & -1 \\ -4 & 3 \end{pmatrix} \begin{pmatrix} x \\ y \end{pmatrix} = \begin{pmatrix} 9 \\ -7 \end{pmatrix}$$

Check by finding the product of the lefthand side.

$$\begin{pmatrix} 3 & -1 \\ -4 & 3 \end{pmatrix} \begin{pmatrix} x \\ y \end{pmatrix} = \begin{pmatrix} 3x - y \\ -4x + 3y \end{pmatrix}$$

2 x 2   2 x 1   2 x 1

answer

Equating the matrices $\begin{pmatrix} 3x & -y \\ -4x + 3y \end{pmatrix} = \begin{pmatrix} 9 \\ -7 \end{pmatrix}$

We have $3x - y = 9$

$-4x + 3y = -7$

$$\begin{pmatrix} 3 & -1 \\ -4 & 3 \end{pmatrix} \begin{pmatrix} x \\ y \end{pmatrix} \begin{pmatrix} 9 \\ -7 \end{pmatrix}$$

If $A = \begin{pmatrix} 3 & -1 \\ -4 & 3 \end{pmatrix}$ then $A^{-1} = \begin{pmatrix} \dfrac{3}{5} & \dfrac{1}{5} \\ \dfrac{4}{5} & \dfrac{3}{5} \end{pmatrix}$

89

premultiply each side above by A^{-1}

$$A^{-1} \begin{pmatrix} 3 & -1 \\ -4 & 3 \end{pmatrix} \begin{pmatrix} x \\ y \end{pmatrix} = A^{-1} \begin{pmatrix} 9 \\ -7 \end{pmatrix}$$

$$I \begin{pmatrix} x \\ y \end{pmatrix} = \begin{pmatrix} \dfrac{3}{5} & \dfrac{1}{5} \\ \dfrac{4}{5} & \dfrac{3}{5} \end{pmatrix} \begin{pmatrix} 9 \\ -7 \end{pmatrix}$$

$$\begin{pmatrix} x \\ y \end{pmatrix} = \begin{pmatrix} \dfrac{27}{5} - \dfrac{7}{5} \\ \dfrac{36}{5} - \dfrac{21}{5} \end{pmatrix} = \begin{pmatrix} \dfrac{20}{5} \\ \dfrac{15}{5} \end{pmatrix}$$

$$\begin{pmatrix} x \\ y \end{pmatrix} = \begin{pmatrix} 4 \\ 3 \end{pmatrix}$$

$x = 4.$

$y = 3$

e. **Relates the use of matrices to simple technical problems**

AN EXAMPLE USING h-PARMETERS

The hybrid parameters or h-parameters of a network are given in a matrix form as

$$\begin{pmatrix} h_{11} & h_{12} \\ h_{12} & h_{22} \end{pmatrix}$$

The input voltage and the output current of a network are expressed in terms of the input current and the output voltage

$$V_1 = I_1 h_{11} + h_{12} V_2$$

$$I_2 = I_1 h_{21} + h_{22} V_2$$

these equations can be written in matrix form as

$$\begin{pmatrix} V_1 \\ I_2 \end{pmatrix} = \begin{pmatrix} h_{11} & h_{12} \\ h_{21} & h_{22} \end{pmatrix} \begin{pmatrix} I_1 \\ V_2 \end{pmatrix}$$

The a.c. equivalent circuit of an a.c. amplifier using h-parameters is given

$$V_{be} = h_{ie} i_b + h_{re} V_{ce}$$

$$i_c = h_{fe} i_b + h_{oe} V_{ce}$$

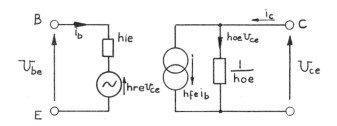

Fig. 46

AN EXAMPLE USING KIRCHOFF'S LAWS

$$V_1 = I_1 r_1 + (I_1 + I_2) R_L$$

$$V_1 = I_1 (r_1 + R_L) + I_2) R_L$$

$$V_2 = I_2 r_2 + (I_1 + I_2) R_L$$

$$V_2 = I_1 R_L + I_2 (r_2 + R_L)$$

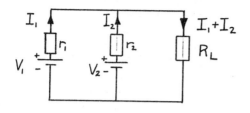

$$V_1 = I_1 (r_1 + R_L) + I_2 R_L$$

$$V_2 = I_1 \ r_1 + I_2 (r_2 + R_L)$$

These equations in matrix form are written

$$\begin{pmatrix} V_1 \\ V_2 \end{pmatrix} = \begin{pmatrix} r_1 \ R_1 & -R_{\underline{L}} \\ r_1 & r_2 \ + \ R_{\underline{L}} \end{pmatrix} \begin{pmatrix} I_1 \\ I_2 \end{pmatrix}$$

To find I_1 and I_2, we have to find first the inverse matrix of

$$\begin{pmatrix} r_1 \ + \ RL & RL \\ r_1 & r_2 \ + \ RL \end{pmatrix} = M$$

pre-multiplying by M^{-1}

$$M^{-1} \begin{pmatrix} V_1 \\ V_2 \end{pmatrix} = M \begin{pmatrix} I_1 \\ I_2 \end{pmatrix}$$

and hence I_1 and I_2 may be calculated.

EXERCISES 6

1. Solve the following simultaneous linear equations:-

   (i) $2x - y = 5$ (ii) $- 3x + 2y = 2$

          $x + y = - 7$ $x - 3y = 5$

   using the elimination and substitution method of algebra.

2. Solve the simultaneous linear equations of question 1 using determinants.

3. Write down the minors and hence the cofactors of the matrices:

   (i) $A = \begin{pmatrix} 1 & 2 \\ 3 & 4 \end{pmatrix}$ and   (ii) $M = \begin{pmatrix} -1 & -2 \\ -3 & 4 \end{pmatrix}$.

4. Determine the adjoint matrices of 3(i) and 3(ii)

5. Find the inverse matrices of the following

   (i) $\begin{pmatrix} 2 & -1 \\ 2 & 1 \end{pmatrix}$ (ii) $\begin{pmatrix} -3 & 2 \\ 1 & -3 \end{pmatrix}$.

6. Solve the simultaneous linear equations of question 1 using matrices.

7. Determine the currents I_1 and I_2 of the network using

   (i) Determinants   (ii) Matrices

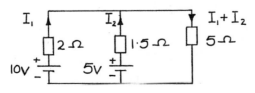

Fig. 48

93

8.   Determine (i) $\dfrac{V_{ce}}{V_{ce}}$ (ii) $\dfrac{i_c}{i_b}$ for the network

where $V_{ce} = -1000\,i_c$

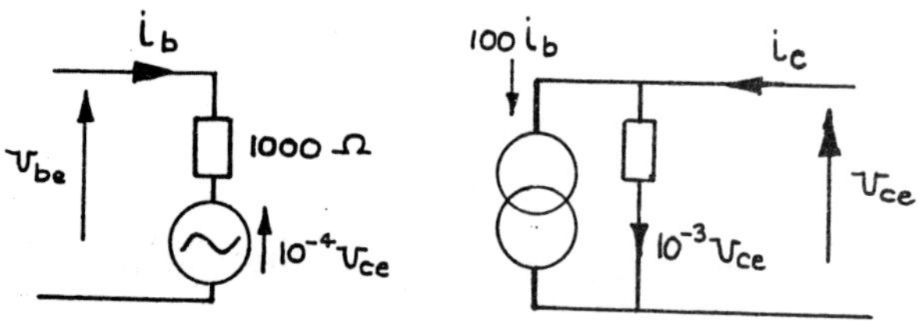

Fig. 49

7.   BINOMIAL THEOREM

Understands and uses the binomial theorem

a.   Expands expressions of the form $(a + x)^n$ for small positive integer n.

b.   States the general form for the binomial coefficents for all positive integer n.

c.   Expands expressions of the form $(1 + x)^n$ where n takes positive, negative or fractional values.

d.   States the range of values of x for which the series is convergent.

e.   Calculates the effect on the subject of a formula when one or more of the independent variables is subject to a small change or error.

BINOMIAL EXPANSION (Sir Isaac Newton 1642 - 1727)

BINOMIAL is an expression containing two terms from basic algerbra we have learnt that the expansion $(a + b)^2 = (a + b)(a + b) = a^2 + ab + ab + b^2$ and therefore $(a + b)^2 = a^2 + 2ab + b^2$, the student should remember this expansion, that is, the squared of the first team *(a)* plus twice the product of the first term (a) and second term (b) plus the squared of the second term (b), namely $(a + b)^2 \equiv a^2 + 2ab + b^2$ there are three terms.

What is the expansion of $(a + b)^3$?

$$(a + b)^3 = (a + b)^2 (a + b) = (a^2 + 2ab + b^2)(a + b)$$

$$= a^3 + 2a^2 b + ab^2 + a^2 b + 2ab^2 + b^3$$

$(a + b)^3 = a^3 + 3a^2 b + 3ab^2 + b^3$, there are four terms

The expansion of $a + b$ to a power greater than three can be found. The binomial expansion for $(1 + x)^n$ is stated:-

$$(1 + x)^n = 1 + nx + \frac{n(n-1)}{1 \times 2} x^2 + \frac{n(n-1)(n-2)}{1 \times 2 \times 3} x^3 + \dots + x^n.$$

There are $n + 1$ terms if n is a positive integer, but there are infinite terms if n is not a positive integer and x lies between -1 and +1.

The binomial expansion for simple positive integer values of n and including the general x^r is given.

$$(1 + x)^n = 1 + nx + \frac{n\,(n\,-\,1)}{1 \times 2}\,x^2 + \frac{n\,(n\,-\,1)\,(n\,-\,2)}{1 \times 2 \times 3}\,x^3 + \ldots$$

$$+\; \frac{n\,(n\,-\,1\,(n\,-\,1\,(n\,-\,2)\,\ldots[n\,-\,(r\,-\,1)]}{1 \times 2 \times 3 \times \ldots xr}\,x^r + \ldots + x^n.$$

Note that 1 x 2 can be written as 2! (factorial two)
1 x 2 x 3 = 3! (factorial three), 1 x 2 x 3 x ...xn = n! (factorial n). The above expansion can be written as

$$(1 + x)^n = \frac{1\,x^0}{0!} + \frac{n}{1!}\,x^1 + \frac{n\,(n\,-\,1)}{2!}\,x^2 + \frac{n\,(n\,-\,1)\,(n\,-\,3)}{3!}\,x^3 + \ldots$$

$$+\; \frac{n\,(n\,-\,1)\,\ldots[n\,-\,(r\,-\,1)]\,x^r}{r!} + \ldots + \frac{n!\,x^n}{n!}$$

The following observations are made:-

1.   The powers of x are in ascending order

        $0, 1, 2, \ldots, n$

2.   The factorial number is the same as that of the power

3.   The coefficients of x^3 are three factors $n\,(n - 1)\,(n - 2)$ that of x^5 are $n(n - 1)\,(n - 2)\,(n - 3)\,(n - 4)$, five factors.

The expansion is written simply as:-

$$(1 + x)^n = 1 + n\,x + \frac{n\,(n\,-\,1)}{2!}\,x^2 + \frac{n\,(n\,-\,1)\,(n\,-\,2)}{3!}\,x^3 + \ldots$$

$$+\; \frac{n\,(n\,-\,1)\,\ldots[n\,-\,(r\,-\,1)]}{r!}\,x^r + \ldots + x^n.$$

Obtains the coefficients of the powers of x using Pascal's triangle.

Blaise Pascal (1623 - 1662). The following expansions are written by referring to the Pascal's triangle.

$(1 +)^0 = 1$

$(1 + x)^1 = 1 + x$

$(1 + x)^2 = 1 + 2x + x^2$

$(1 + x)^3 = 1 + 3x + 3x^2 + x^3$

$(1 + x)^4 = 1 + 4x + 6x^2 + 4x^3 + x^4$

$(1 \times x)^5 = 1 + 5x + 10x^3 + 5x^4 + x^5$

$(1 + x)^6 = 1 + 6x + 15x^2 + 20x^3 + 15x^4 + 6x^5 + x^6$

$(1 + x)^7 = 1 + 7x + 21x^2 + 35x^3 + 35x^4 + 21x^5 + 7x^6 + x^7$

$(1 + x)^8 = 1 + 8x + 28x^2 + 56x^3 + 70x^4 + 56x^5 + 28x^6 + 8x^7 + x^8$

$(1 + x)^9 = 1 + 9x + 36x^2 + 84x^3 + 126x^4 + 126x^5 + 84x^6 + 36x^7 + 9x^8 + x^9$

$(1 + x)^{10} = 1 + 10x + 45x^2 + 120x^3 + 120x^4 + 252x^5 + 210x^6 + 120x^7 + 45x^8 + 10x^9 + x^{10}$

97

Pascal's triangle.

$$1$$

$$1 \quad 1$$

$$1 \quad 2 \quad 1$$

$$1 \quad 3 \quad 3 \quad 1$$

$$1 \quad 4 \quad 6 \quad 4 \quad 1$$

$$1 \quad 5 \quad 10 \quad 10 \quad 5 \quad 1$$

$$1 \quad 6 \quad 15 \quad 20 \quad 15 \quad 6 \quad 1$$

$$1 \quad 7 \quad 21 \quad 35 \quad 35 \quad 21 \quad 7 \quad 1$$

$$1 \quad 8 \quad 28 \quad 56 \quad 70 \quad 56 \quad 28 \quad 8 \quad 1$$

$$1 \quad 9 \quad 36 \quad 84 \quad 126 \quad 126 \quad 84 \quad 36 \quad 9 \quad 1$$

$$1 \quad 10 \quad 45 \quad 120 \quad 210 \quad 252 \quad 210 \quad 120 \quad 45 \quad 10 \quad 1$$

The following can be observed from the above triangle:

1.   We write I_s along the sides of the triangle.

2.   The first 1 is the answer to the expansion
        $(1 + x)^\circ = 1$, any number raised to the power nought is unity.

3.   The second row are the coefficients of $(1 + x)' = 1 + x$, the coefficient of
        x is unity and that of x° is 1.

4.   The third row shows the coefficients of the expansion
        $(1 + x)^2 = 1 + 2x + x^2$, the coefficient of x° is 1, the
        coefficient of x' is 2 and the coefficient of x^2 is unity.

5.   The fourth row has coefficients 1, 3, 3 and 1, the 3 is derived by adding 1
        and 2 from the third row as indicated by the upward arrows and so on.
        Pascal's triangle enables us to write down the binomial expansion upto the
        $n = 10$ without very much trouble for value of n greater than 10, Newton's
        expansion is much easier.

WORKED EXAMPLE 36

Expand $(1 + x)^4, (1 + x)^5, (1 + x)^6, (1 + x)^7, (1 + x)^8 (1 + x)^9 (1 + x)^{10}$

using Newton's expansion method.

SOLUTION 36

$$(1 + x)^4 = 1 + 4x + \frac{4 \times 3}{1 \times 2}x^2 + \frac{4 \times 3 \times 2}{1 \times 2 \times 3}x^3 + \frac{4 \times 3 \times 2 \times 1}{1 \times 2 \times 3 \times 4}x^4$$

$$= 1 + 4x + 6\,x^2 + 4\,x^3 + x^4$$

$$(1 + x)^5 = 1 + 5x + \frac{5 \times 4}{1 \times 2}x^2 + \frac{5 \times 4 \times 3}{1 \times 2 \times 3}x^3 + \frac{5 \times 4 \times 3 \times 2}{1 \times 2 \times 3 \times 4}x^4 + x^5$$

$$= 1 + 5x + 10\,x^2 + 10\,x^3 + 5\,x^4 + x^5$$

$$(1 + x)^6 = 1 + 6x + \frac{6 \times 5}{1 \times 2}x^2 + \frac{6 \times 5 \times 4}{1 \times 2 \times 3}x^3 + \frac{6 \times 5 \times 4}{1 \times 2 \times 3}x^4 + \frac{6\,x\,5 \times 4 \times 3}{1 \times 2 \times 3 \times 4}x^5 + x^6$$

$$= 1 + 6x + 15\,x^2 + 20\,x\,3 + 20\,x^4 + 15\,x^5 + x^6$$

$$= (1 + 7)x + 21\,x^2 + 35\,x^3 + 35\,x^4 + 21\,x^5 + 7\,x^6 + x^7$$

$$(1 + x)^8 = 1 + 8x + \frac{8 \times 7}{1 \times 2}x^2 + \frac{8 \times 7 \times 6}{1 \times 2 \times 3}x^3 + \frac{8 \times 7 \times 6 \times 5}{1 \times 2 \times 3x\,4}x^4 + \frac{8 \times 7 \times 6 \times 5 \times 4}{1 \times 2 \times 3 \times 4 \times 5}x^5$$

$$+ \frac{8 \times 7 \times 6 \times 5 \times 4 \times 3}{1 \times 2 \times 3 \times 4 \times 5 \times 6}x^6 + \frac{8 \times 7 \times 6 \times 5 \times 4 \times 3 \times 2}{1 \times 2 \times 3 \times 4 \times 5 \times 6 \times 7}x^7 + x^8$$

$$= 1 + 8\,x + 28\,x^2 + 56\,x^3 + 70\,x^4 + 56\,x^5 + 28\,x^6 + 8\,x^7 + x^8$$

$$(1 + x)^9 = 1 + 9x + \frac{9 \times 8}{1 \times 2}x^2 + \frac{9 \times 8 \times 7}{1 \times 2 \times 3}x^3 + \frac{9 \times 8 \times 7 \times 6}{1 \times 2 \times 3 \times 4}x^4 + \frac{9 \times 8 \times 7 \times 6x\,5}{1 \times 2 \times 3 \times 4 \times 5}x^5$$

$$+ \frac{9 \times 8 \times 7 \times 6 \times 5 \times 4}{1 \times 2 \times 3 \times 4 \times 5 \times 6} x^6 + \frac{9 \times 8 \times 7 \times 6 \times 5 \times 5 \times 3}{1 \times 2 \times 3 \times 4 \times 5 \times 6 \times 7} x^7$$

$$+ \frac{9 \times 8 \times 7 \times 6 \times 5 \times 4 \times 3 \times 2}{1 \times 2 \times 3 \times 4 \times 5 \times 6 \times 7 \times 8} x^8 + x^9$$

$$= 1 + 9x + 36\, x^2 + 84\, x^3 + 126\, x^4 + 126\, x^5 + 84\, x^6 + 36\, x^7 + 9\, x^8 + x^9$$

$$(1 + x)^{10} = 1 + 10x + 45\, x^2 + 120\, x^3 + 210\, x^4 + 252\, x^5 + 210\, x^6 + 120\, x^2$$

$$+ 45\, x^8 + 10\, x^9 + x^{10}.$$

Rewrites $(a + bx)^n = a^n (1 + Z)^n$ where $Z = \frac{b}{a} x$ and hence expands more general binomial expressions.

$$(a + bx)^n = \left[a \left(1 + \frac{b}{a} x \right) \right]^n = a^n \left(1 + \frac{b}{a} x \right)^n = a^n (1 + Z)^n$$

where $Z = \frac{b}{a} x$.

WORKED EXAMPLE 37

Expand the following Binomial expressions:

(i) $(x + 2y)^4$ (ii) $(3x - 2y)^5$ using the above technique.

SOLUTION 37

(i) $(x + 2y)^4 = [x(1 + 2\, y/x)]^4 = x^4 \ (1 + Z)^4$

where $Z = 2\, y/x$

$(1 + Z)^4 = 1 + 4Z + 6 Z^2 + 4Z^3 + Z^4$

therefore $(x + 2y)^4 = x^4 (1 + Z)^4 = x^4 (1 + 4Z + 6Z^2 + 4Z^3 + Z^4)$

$$= x^4 \left[1 + 4 \left(\frac{2y}{x} \right) + 6 \left(\frac{2y}{x} \right)^2 + 4 \left(\frac{2y}{x^3} \right)^3 + \left(\frac{2y}{x} \right)^4 \right]$$

$$= x^4 \left[1 + 8\frac{y}{x} + 24\, \frac{y^2}{x^2} + 32\, \frac{y^3}{x^3} + 16\, \frac{y^4}{x^4} \right]$$

$$= x^4 + 8y\,x^3 + 24\,y^2\,x^2 + 32\,y^3\,x + 16\,y^4$$

(ii) $$(3x - 2y)^5 = \left[3x\left(\frac{1 - 2y}{3x}\right)\right]^5 = 3^5\,x^5\left[1 + \left(\frac{-2y}{3x}\right)\right]^5$$

$$(1 + Z)^5 = 1 + 5\,Z + 10\,Z^2 + 10\,Z^3 + 5\,Z^4 + Z^5$$

$$= 1 + 5\left(\frac{-2y}{2x}\right) + 10\left(\frac{-2y}{3x}\right)^2 + 10\left(\frac{-2y}{3x}\right)^3 + 5\left(\frac{2y}{3x}\right)^4 + \left(\frac{-2y}{3x}\right)^5$$

$$= 1 - \frac{10y}{3x} + \frac{40}{9}\frac{y^2}{x^2} - \frac{80}{27}\frac{y^3}{x^3} + \frac{80}{81}\frac{y^4}{x^4} - \frac{32}{243}\frac{y^5}{x^5}$$

$$(3x - 2y)^5 = 243\,x^5\left(1 - \frac{10}{3}\frac{y}{x} + \frac{40}{9}\frac{y^2}{x^2} - \frac{80}{27}\frac{y^3}{x^3} + \frac{80}{81}\frac{y^4}{x^4} - \frac{32}{243}\frac{y^5}{x^5}\right)$$

$$= 243\,x^5 - 810\,y\,x^4 + 1080\,y^2\,x^3 - 720\,x^2\,y^3 + 240\,y^4\,x - 32\,y^5.$$

Obtains the first few terms of the infinite expansions of
$(1 + x)^n$ which pertain when n is other than a positive integer

The expansion of $(1 + x)^n$ when n is not a positive integer, is an infinite series of terms.

$$(1 + x)^n = 1 + nx + n\,(n - 1)\,\frac{x^2}{2!} + n\,(-1)\,(n - 2)\,\frac{x^3}{3!} + \dots$$

the values of x are small and lie between -1 and +1, that is,

$$-1 < x < 1$$

WORKED EXAMPLE 38

Obtain the first five terms of the infinite series expansion of $\sqrt{\dfrac{1 + x}{1 - x}}$.

SOLUTION 38

$$\sqrt{\frac{1+x}{1-x}} = \frac{(1+x)^{1/2}}{(1-x)^{1/2}} = (1+x)^{1/2}(1-x)^{-1/2} \quad \text{where}$$

$$(1+x)^{1/2} = 1 + \frac{1}{2}x + \frac{1}{2}\left(\frac{1}{2}-1\right)x^2\frac{1}{2!} + \frac{1}{2}\left(\frac{1}{2}-2\right)x^3\frac{1}{3!}$$

$$+ \frac{1}{2}\left(\frac{1}{2}-1\right)\left(\frac{1}{2}-2\right)\left(\frac{1}{2}-3\right)x^4\frac{1}{4!}$$

$$= 1 + \frac{1}{2}x - \frac{1}{8}x^2 + \frac{1}{16}x^3 - \frac{5}{128}x^4$$

$$(1-x)^{-1/2} = 1 + \left(-\frac{1}{2}\right)(-x) + \left(-\frac{1}{2}\right)(-1)(-x)^2\frac{1}{2!} + \left(-\frac{1}{2}\right)\left(-\frac{1}{2}-1\right)\left(-\frac{1}{2}-2\right)(-x)^3$$

$$+ \left(-\frac{1}{2}\right)\left(-\frac{1}{2}-1\right)\left(-\frac{1}{2}-2\right)\left(-\frac{1}{2}-3\right)(-x)^4\frac{1}{4!}.$$

WORKED EXAMPLE 39

Write down the first four terms in the binomial expansion of the following:-

(i) $(1-x)^{-2}$ 　(ii) $\left(1+\frac{1}{3}x\right)^{-3}$ 　(iii) $(3-x)^{1/2}$.

SOLUTION 39

(i) $(1-x)^{-2} = 1 + (-2)(-x) + (-2)(-3)(-x)^2\frac{1}{2} + (-2)(-3)(-4)(-x)^3$

$$= 1 + 2x + 3x^2 + 4x^3$$

(ii)

$$\left(1+\frac{1}{3}x\right)^{-3} = 1 + (-3)\left(\frac{1}{3}x\right) + (-3)(-4)\left(\frac{1}{3}x\right)^2\frac{1}{2} + (-3)(-4)(-5)\left(\frac{1}{3}x\right)^3\frac{1}{1.}$$

$$= 1 - x + \frac{2}{3}x^2 - \frac{10}{27}x^3$$

(iii) $(3 - x)^{1/2} = 3^{1/2}\left(1 - \frac{x}{3}\right)^{1/2} = 3^{1/2}\left(1 + \left(\frac{1}{2}\right)\right)\left(-\frac{x}{3}\right) + \left(\frac{1}{2}\right)\left(-\frac{1}{2}\right)\left(-\frac{x}{3}\right)^2 \frac{1}{2}$$

$$+ \frac{1}{2}\left(-\frac{1}{2}\right)\frac{\left(-\frac{3}{2}\right)\left(-\frac{x}{3}\right)^3}{3!}$$

$$= 3^{1/2}\left(1 - \frac{x}{6} - \frac{1}{72}x^2 - \frac{1}{216}x^3\right).$$

Obtain similar expansions for $(a + bx)^n$ states the validity condition for such infinite expansions

$$(a + bx)^n = \left[a\left(1 + \frac{bx}{a}\right)\right]^n = a^n\left(1 + \frac{bx}{a}\right)^n = a^n(1 + z)^n$$

where $z = \frac{bx}{a}$ and n is not a positive integer

$$(1 + z)^n = 1 + nz + n(n - 1)z^2\frac{1}{2!} + n(n - 1)(n - 2)z^3\frac{1}{3!} + \dots$$

which is an infinite series of expansion.

WORKED EXAMPLE 40

Find the first four terms in the expansion $(3 - 2x)^{-2}$ as a series in ascending powers of x, and write down the first fours terms in the expansion of $(3 + 2x)^{-2}$.

Find the range of values for which both the above expansions are valid.

SOLUTION 40

$$(3 - 2x)^{-2} = 3^2\left(1 - 2\frac{x}{3}\right)^2 = \frac{1}{9}\left(1 - 2\frac{x}{3}\right)^2$$

$$\left(1 - 2\frac{x}{3}\right)^{-2} = 1 + (-2)\left(-2\frac{x}{3}\right) + (-2)(-3)\left(-2\frac{x}{3}\right)^2\frac{1}{2!} + (-2)(-3)(-4)\left(-2\frac{x}{3}\right)^3 \cdots$$

$$= 1 + \frac{4}{3}x - \frac{4}{3}x^2 + \frac{32}{27}x^3.$$

$$(3 - 2x)^{-2} = \frac{1}{9}\left(1 + \frac{4}{3}x - \frac{4}{3}x^2 + \frac{32}{27}x^3\right)$$

$$= \frac{1}{9} + \frac{4}{27}x - 4\frac{4}{27}x^2 + \frac{32}{243}x^3$$

The expansion is valid for values of x such that

$$-1 < \frac{-2x}{3} < 1 \quad \text{from which} \quad -1 < -\frac{2x}{3} \quad \text{and} \quad \frac{-2x}{3} < 1$$

$$-1 < -2\frac{x}{3}, 1 > 2\frac{x}{3} \quad \text{or} \quad x < \frac{3}{2}$$

$$-\frac{2x}{3} < 1, -2x < 3, \quad \text{or} \quad x > -\frac{3}{2}$$

therefore $-3/2 < x < 3/2$, that is, x lies between $-3/2$ and $3/2$.

$$(3 + 2x)^{-2} = \frac{1}{9} - \frac{4}{27}x + \frac{4}{27}x^2 - \frac{32}{243}x^3$$

the signs change from the previous expansion except the first term which remains at 1/9.

This expansion is valid for values of x such that $-1 < \frac{2x}{3} < 1$

or for $-\frac{3}{2} < x < \frac{3}{2}$.

Therefore x lies between -3/2 and 3/2 for both expansions.

Applies the binomial theorem to the calculation of certain roots to a desired degree of accuracy and to the simplification of certain formulae by first or second order approximations.

We have seen that the binomial theorem is

$$(1 + x)^n = 1 + nx + n(n-1)x^2\frac{1}{2!} + n(n-1)(n-2)x^3\frac{1}{3!} + \ldots$$

an infinite series when n is not a positive integer and x lies between -1 and +1.

If $x < < 1$ then we can approximate the expansion $(1 + x)^n \approx 1 + nx + n(n-1)\frac{x^2}{2}$ a second order approximation or further still to a first order approximation $(1 + x)^n \approx 1 + nx$.

WORKED EXAMPLE 41

Use the binomial theorem to find the value to five significant figures of

(i) $(1.003)^{-1/5}$ (ii) $(1.02)^{1/4}$ (iii) $(1.0001)^{-1/7}$.

SOLUTION 41

(i) $(1.003)^{1/5} = (1 + 0.003)^{1/5} = 1 + \left(-\frac{1}{5}\right)(0.003) + \left(-\frac{1}{5}\right)\left(-\frac{1}{5} - 1\right)(0.003)^2\frac{1}{2!}$

$(1.003)^{-1/5} \approx 1 - \frac{1}{5}0.003 + \left(-\frac{1}{5}\right)\left(-\frac{9}{5}\right)0.000009\left(\frac{1}{2}\right)$

$$= 1 - 0.0006 + \frac{9}{25 \times 2} \times 0.000009$$

$= 1 - 0.0006 + 0.00000162$

$\approx 0.9994016 \approx 0.9994$ to five significant figures.

If we use $(1 + x)^n \approx 1 + nx$

$$(1 + 0.003)^{-1/5} \approx 1 - \frac{1}{5}\, 0.003 = 1 - 0.0006 = 0.9994$$

so in this case we used the first order approximation it would have been sufficient to obtain an accuracy to five significant figures.

If the answer were required to seven significant figures, we should take the second order approximation

$$(1.003)^{-1/5} \approx 0.9994016 \approx 0.999402.$$

The calculator gives $(1.003)^{-1/5} = 0.999401.$

EXERCISES 7

1. Write down the first three terms in the expansion, in ascending powers of x for the following binomial expressions:-

(i) $(1 - 5x)^{-3}$ (ii) $(1 + 3x)^{3/4}$ (iii) $(1 - 4x)^{-1/3}$

(iv) $(1 - x)^{1/2}$ (v) $(1 + x)^{-1/2}$.

2. Find the first three non-zero terms in the expansions in ascending powers of x:

(i) $(1 + px)^n$ (ii) $(1 - px)^{-n}$
(iii) $(1 + 3\,ax)^{-n}$
(iv) $(1 - 2\,bx)^n$ (v) $(1 - bx)^{+n}$.

3. Find the first three non-zero terms in the following expansions, in ascending powers of y:

(i) $\sqrt{\dfrac{1 - y}{1 + y}}$ (ii) $\dfrac{1}{\sqrt{1 - y^2}}$ (iii) $\sqrt{9 + ay}$ (iv) $\dfrac{1}{\sqrt{16 - by.}}$

4. Expand $(25 + x)^{1/2}$ in ascending powers of x up to and including the term in x^3.

5. Expand in ascending powers of x up to and including the term in x^3.

(i) $(1 + 2x)^{1/3}$ (ii) $(1 - 3x)^{-1/5}$.

Given that $(1 + 2x)^{1/3} + 25(1 - 3x)^{-1/5}$
$= a + bx + cx^2 + dx^3 + \ldots$, find the numerical values of a, b, c and d.

6. Find the coefficients of x^3 in the expansions:

(i) $(1 + 2x)^{1/2} (1 - 3x)^{-1/2}$ (ii) $(1 - x)^{-1/2} (1 + x)^{-1/2}$ (iii) $\dfrac{1 - x}{(1 + x)^3}$.

7. Expand $(1 - 7x)^{-1/3}$ in ascending powers of x up to and including the terms in x^3.

8. Write down the term containing b^r in the binomial expansion of $(a + b)^n$ where n is a positive integer.

9. Write down the coefficient of x^{25} in the binomial expansion of $(1 - 3x)^{37}$.

10. The period T of a simple pendulum is given by the formula $T = 2\pi \sqrt{l/g}$ where l is the length of the pendulum and g is the acceleration due to gravity.

   It is required to calculate g from the formula above.

   If errors of $+ 1\%$ in T and -0.5% in l are made, use the binomial expansions to determine the percentage error in the calculated value g, giving your answer correct to three 'decimal places.

11. It is required to determine l from the formula $f = K \dfrac{\sqrt{w}}{l}$

   If errors of -2% in l and $+ 1\%$ in w are made, use the binomial expansion, to find the percentage error in the calculated value of f. (Hint expand $(1 + x)^{1/2}$ and $(1 - 2x)^{-1}$ in ascending powers of x up to and and including the term in x^2).

12. Write down and simplify the first four terms in the expansion of $(1 + x)^n$ in ascending powers of x when $n = 3$, $n = -3$ and when $n = -1/3$.

13. Find correct to 4 decimal places the values of

   (i) $\dfrac{1}{(1.005)^3}$ (ii) $\sqrt[3]{27.003}$ (iii) $(1.05)^{1/5}$ (iv) $0.995^{-1/3}$.

14. Express (i) $(1 + x)^{1/2}$ and (ii) $(1 - x)^{-3}$ as series of ascending powers of x, in each case up to and including the term in x^2.

   Hence show that, if x is small $\dfrac{(1 + x)^{1/2}}{(1 - x)^3} = 1 + \dfrac{7}{2}x + \dfrac{59}{8}x^2$.

   Calculate the percentage change which occurs in the value of $\dfrac{w^{1/2}}{z^3}$ if w is increased by 1% and z is decreased by 1%.

15. Expand $(1 + bx)^{-n}$ in ascending power of x up to and including the term in x^3. Given that the first four terms are $1 + 5x + 9x^2 + ax^3$, calculate the values of the constants a, b and n.

16. Find the term independent of x in the expansion of $\left(x - \dfrac{1}{x^2} \right)^5 \left(x + \dfrac{1}{x} \right)^9$.

17. Use the binomial Theorem to find the value, correct to five significant figures, of $(1.003)^{15}$.

18. Find the coefficient of x^4 in the expansion of $(3 - ax)^8$

    Find the coefficient of x^5 in the expansion of $(2a - x)^7$.

    If the two coefficents are equal find the non-zero value of a.

19. Expand $\left(1 + \dfrac{1}{3}x \right)^{-3}$ as far as the term in x^4. Hence, or otherwise, obtain

    the coefficent of x^4 in the expansion of $(1 - x - x^3)\left(1 + \dfrac{1}{3}x \right)^{-3}$, the

    values of x being such as to make the expansions valid.

20. Write down the first four terms in the binomial expansion of $(1 - x)^{-2}$. Use your result to expand $(1 - x - x^2)^{-2}$ as far as the term in x^3, assuming that the values of x are such that the expansion is valid.

21. Find the non-zero value of a if the coefficent of x^3 in the expansion of $(a - x)^5$ is equal to the coefficient of x^4 in the expansion of $(3 - ax)^7$.

8.   THE EXPONENTIAL FUNCTION.

USES THE SERIES EXPANSION OF THE EXPONENTIAL FUNCTION

a.   States the expansion of e^x in a power series

b.   Deduces the expansion of e^{-x}

c.   States that the expansions are convergent for all x.

d.   Deduces the expansion of ae^{kx} where k is positive or negative.

e.   Deduces the series for e and evaluates e four decimal places.

Exponential function is a constant raised to a variable x, that is, a^x is an exponential function where $'a'$ is, a constant and x is a variable, specifically when the constant e is raised to x.

a.   **THE EXPANSION OF** e^x.

$$e^x = 1 + \frac{x}{1!} + \frac{x^2}{2!} + \frac{x^3}{3!} + \frac{x^4}{4!} + \frac{x^5}{5!} + \ldots + \frac{x^r}{r!} + \ldots$$

where $r!$ (read as r factorial)

FACTORIAL

$r! = 1 \times 2 \times 3 \times 4 \times \ldots (r - 1) \, r$
$5! = 1 \times 2 \times 3 \times 4 \times 5$
$4! = 1 \times 2 \times 3 \times 4$
$3! = 1 \times 2 \times 3$
$2! = 1 \times 2$
$1! = 1.$

The first term of this power series is actually $\dfrac{x^o}{0!}$ where $x^o = 1$ and $o! = 1$, to show that $o! = 1$, we have .
$r! = 1 \times 2 \times 3 \, x \ldots (r-1)r = (r = 1)! \, r!$

If $r = 1$, $1! = (1-1)! \, 1$ and therefore $1! = o! = 1$.

This infinite series is called power series since the powers of x are increasing by $1, 0, 1, 2, 3, 4, \ldots$, the powers are ascending.

If $x = 1$ then $\quad e^1 = 1 + \dfrac{1}{1!} + \dfrac{1}{2!} + \dfrac{1}{3!} + \dfrac{1}{4!} + \dfrac{1}{5!} + \ldots$

$$= 1 + 1 + 0.5 + \dfrac{1}{6} + \dfrac{1}{24} + \dfrac{1}{120} + \dfrac{1}{720} + \ldots$$

If we sum all these terms to infinity e will be equal $e = 2.718$.

b. **Deduces the expansion of e^{-x}**

If x is replaced by $-x$ $\quad e^{-x} = 1 + \dfrac{(-x)}{1!} + \dfrac{(-x)^2}{2!} + \dfrac{(-x)^3}{3!} + \dfrac{(-x)^4}{4!} + \ldots$

$$= 1 - \dfrac{x}{1!} + \dfrac{x^2}{2!} - \dfrac{x^3}{3!} + \dfrac{x^4}{4!} + \ldots + (-1)^r \dfrac{x^r}{r!}$$

the general term of this expansion is $\quad (-1)^r \dfrac{x^r}{r!}$ because if $r = 2$, then $\quad (-1)^2 \dfrac{x^2}{2!}$

if $r = 3$ then $\quad (-1)^3 \dfrac{x^3}{3!} = -\dfrac{x^3}{3!}$ $\qquad$ which is the fourth term.

c. **States that the expansions are convergent for all x.**

What is the difference between a convergent and divergent series?

The series $1 + 2 + 3 + 4 + \ldots$ summed up to infinity gives a very large or infinite result, this is a divergent series, the series as it progresses it becomes greater and greater, therefore it diverges.

The series $\quad 1 + 1 + \dfrac{1}{2} + \dfrac{1}{6} + \dfrac{1}{24} + \dfrac{1}{120} + \dfrac{1}{720} + \dfrac{1}{5040} + \ldots \qquad$ as it

progresses it becomes smaller and, therefore it converges, that is, the sum of the infinite terms is finite. Therefore the expansions of e^x are convergent for all x.

d. **Deduces, the expansions of ae^{kx} where k is positive or negative.**

The expansion of ae^{kx} can be similarly stated

$$ae^{kx} = a\left(1 + \dfrac{kx}{1!} + \dfrac{(kx)^2}{2!} + \dfrac{(kx)^3}{3!^3} + \ldots\right)$$

$$= a\left(1 + \frac{kx}{1!} + \frac{k^2 x^2}{2!} + \frac{k^3 x^3}{3!} + \ldots\right)$$

If $K = 2, a = 3$

$$3 e^{2x} = 3\left(1 + \frac{2x}{1!} + \frac{4^2}{2!} + \frac{8 x^3}{3!} + \ldots\right)$$

If $K = -3, a = 3$

$$3 e^{-3x} = 3\left(1 - \frac{3x}{1!} + \frac{9 x^2}{2!} - \frac{27 x^3}{3!} + \frac{81 x^4}{4!} + \ldots\right)$$

e. **Deduces the series for e and evaluates e to four decimal places.**

$$e^1 = 1 + \frac{1}{1!} + \frac{1}{2!} + \frac{1}{3!} + \frac{1}{4!} + \frac{1}{5!} + \ldots$$

$$e^1 = 1 + 1 + 0.5 + 0.1666666 + 0.0416666 + 0.0083333333$$

$$+ 0.00133888889 + 0.000198412 + \ldots$$

$$= 2.7182539 \approx 2.7183$$

Taking eight terms gives approximately 2.7183 correct to 4 decimal places. The value of e lies between 2 and 3.

THE IRRATIONAL NUMBER e

The number e is not a rational number, that is, it cannot be expressed exactly as a ratio. Such as N/D where N and D are integer numbers. The number e is an irrational a number like $\sqrt{2}, \sqrt{3}, \pi$.

WORKED EXAMPLE 42

Determine the values of the following exponential functions:-

(i) e^{-2} (ii) e^3 (iii) $e^{1/4}$, correct to four decimal places by considering 10 terms of the expansion

SOLUTION 42

(i)
$$e^{-2} = 1 + \frac{(-2)}{1} + \frac{(-2)^2}{3!} + \frac{(-2)^3}{3!} + \frac{(-2)^4}{4!} + \frac{(-2)^5}{5!} + \frac{(-2)^6}{6!}$$

$$+ \frac{(-2)^7}{7!} + \frac{(-2)^8}{8!} + \frac{(-2)^9}{9!}$$

$$= 1 - 2 + 2 - 1.3333333 + 0.66666666 - 0.26666666$$

$$+ 0.0888888 - 0.0253968 + 6.349263 \times 10^{-3}$$

$$- 1.4109347 \times 10^{-3}$$

$$= 0.135097 \approx 0.1351.$$

In calculating the above, we perform the calculation as follows:

for example $\frac{(-2)^7}{7!}$ is performed as follows: enter the number 2 by pressing the

2 key then press the minus sign $\boxed{+/-}$, the display shows -2, then press

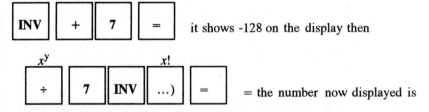

$\boxed{\text{INV}}$ $\boxed{+}$ $\boxed{7}$ $\boxed{=}$ it shows -128 on the display then

$\boxed{\div}^{x^y}$ $\boxed{7}$ $\boxed{\text{INV}}$ $\boxed{\ldots)}^{x!}$ $\boxed{=}$ = the number now displayed is

- 0.0253968, similarly for all the other numbers, adding up the terms give 0.135097 and correct to four decimal places the answer for $e^{-2} = 0.1351$.

The value of e^{-2} $\boxed{2}$ $\boxed{+/-}$ $\boxed{\text{INV}}$ $\boxed{\ln}$ = 0.1353352(directly).

(ii) $\quad e^3 = \dfrac{3}{1!} + \dfrac{3^2}{2!} + \dfrac{3^3}{3!} + \dfrac{3^4}{4!} + \dfrac{3^5}{5!} + \dfrac{3^6}{6!} + \dfrac{3^7}{7!} + \dfrac{3^8}{8!} + \dfrac{3^9}{9!}$

$= 1 + 3 + 4.5 + 4.5 + 3.375 + 2.025 + 1.0125 + 0.4339285 + 0.1627232$
$+ 0.054241 = 20.063393$ or 20.0634 correct to four decimal places.

e^3 directly is found, $\boxed{3}\ \boxed{\text{INV}}\ \boxed{\text{ln}}$ is 20.085537.

(iii) $\quad e^{\frac{1}{4}} = 1 + \dfrac{\frac{1}{4}}{1!} + \dfrac{(\frac{1}{4})^2}{2!} + \dfrac{(\frac{1}{4})^3}{3!} + \dfrac{(\frac{1}{4})^4}{4!} + \dfrac{(\frac{1}{4})^5}{5!} + \dfrac{(\frac{1}{4})^6}{6!} + \dfrac{(\frac{1}{4})^7}{7!} + \dfrac{(\frac{1}{4})^8}{8!} + \dfrac{(\frac{1}{4})^9}{9!}$

$= 1 + \dfrac{1}{4} + \dfrac{1}{32} + \dfrac{1}{384} + \dfrac{1}{6144} + \dfrac{1}{122880}$ negligible terms

$= 1.2840251$ or 1.2840 correct to four decimal places $e^{\frac{1}{4}} = 1.2840254$ by

pressing $\boxed{.}\ \boxed{2}\ \boxed{5}\ \boxed{\text{INV}}\ \boxed{\overset{e^x}{\text{ln}}}$

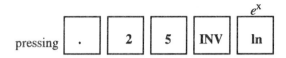

WORKED EXAMPLE 43

Write down the first five terms of the expansions of the following exponential functions without evaluating.

(i) $\quad e^{1/2}$ (ii) $e^{-1/2}$ (ii) $e^{1/3}$ (iv) $e^{1/5}$ (v) e^5

SOLUTIONS 43

(i) $\quad e^{1/2} = 1 + \dfrac{1/2}{1!} + \dfrac{(1/2)^2}{2!} + \dfrac{(1/2)^3}{3!} + \dfrac{(1/2)^4}{4!}$

$= 1 + \dfrac{1}{2 \times 1!} + \dfrac{1}{2^2 \times 2!} + \dfrac{1}{2^3 \times 3!} + \dfrac{1}{2^4 \times 4!}$

(ii) $\quad e^{1/2} = 1 + \dfrac{(-1/2)}{1!} + \dfrac{(-1/2)^2}{2!} + \dfrac{(-1/2)^3}{3!} + \dfrac{(-1/2)^4}{4!}$

$= 1 - \dfrac{1}{2 \times 1!} + \dfrac{1}{2^2 \times 2!} - \dfrac{1}{2^3 \times 3!} + \dfrac{1}{2^4 \times 4!}$

114

(iii) $\quad e^{1/3} = 1 + \dfrac{1/3}{1!} + \dfrac{(1/3)^2}{2!} + \dfrac{(1/3)^3}{3!} + \dfrac{(1/3)^4}{4!}$

$\quad\quad = \dfrac{1}{3 \times 1!} + \dfrac{1}{3^2 \times 2!} + \dfrac{1}{3^3 \times 3!} \ \dfrac{1}{3^4 \times 4!}$

(iv) $\quad e^{1/5} = 1 + \dfrac{\dfrac{1}{5}}{1!} + \dfrac{\left(\dfrac{1}{5}\right)^2}{2!} + \dfrac{\left(\dfrac{1}{5}\right)^3}{3!} + \dfrac{\left(\dfrac{1}{5}\right)^4}{4!}$

$\quad\quad = \dfrac{1}{5 \, x \, 1!} + \dfrac{1}{5^2 x \, 2!} + \dfrac{1}{5^3 x \, 3!} + \dfrac{1}{5^4 x \, 4!}$

(v) $\quad e^5 = 1 + \dfrac{5}{1!} + \dfrac{5^2}{2!} + \dfrac{5^3}{3!} + \dfrac{5^4}{4!}.$

WORKED EXAMPLE 44

Determine the series for (i) $\quad \cosh 2x = \dfrac{e^{2x} + e^{-2x}}{2}$ and

(ii) $\quad \sinh 3x = \dfrac{1}{2}\left(e^{3x} - e^{-3x}\right)$ by writing 5 terms for each expansion.

SOLUTION 44

(i) $\quad \cosh 2x = \dfrac{e^{2x} + e^{-2x}}{2} = \dfrac{1}{2}\left[1 + 2\,\dfrac{x}{1} + \dfrac{(2x)^2}{2!} + \dfrac{(2x)^3}{3!} + \dfrac{(2x)^4}{4!}\right]$

$\quad + \dfrac{1}{2}\left[1 - 2\,\dfrac{x}{1!} + \dfrac{(2x)^2}{2!} - \dfrac{(2x)^3}{3!} + \dfrac{(2x)^4}{4!}\right] = \dfrac{1}{2}\left(2 + 2\dfrac{(x)^2}{2!} + \dfrac{2\,(x)^4}{4!}\right)$

$\quad \cosh 2\,x = 1 + \dfrac{(2x)^2}{2!} + \dfrac{(2x)^4}{4!}\ .$

(i) $\quad \sinh 3x = \dfrac{1}{2}\left(e^{3x} - e^{-3x}\right) = \dfrac{1}{2}\left[1 + \dfrac{3x}{1!} + \dfrac{(3x)^2}{2!} + \dfrac{(3x)^3}{3!} + \dfrac{(3x)^4}{4!}\right]$

$\quad - \dfrac{1}{2}\left(1 - \dfrac{3x}{1!} + \dfrac{(3x)^2}{2!} - \dfrac{(3x)^3}{3!} + \dfrac{(3x)^4}{4!}\right)$

$\quad \sinh 3x = \dfrac{1}{2}\left(2\,\dfrac{3x}{1} + 2\,\dfrac{(3x)^3}{3!}\right) = 3x - \dfrac{(3x)^3}{3!}.$

EXERCISE 8

1. Write down the first five terms for the expansion e^x.

2. Write down the first five terms for the expansion e^{-x}.

3. Write down the first five terms for the expansion e^{-1} and hence evaluate correct to five significant figures.

4. Write down the first five terms for the following expansions:

$$\text{(i)} \ e \quad \text{(ii)} \ \frac{1}{e} \quad \text{(iii)} \ \frac{1}{e^2} \quad \text{(iv)} \ \frac{1}{2}\left(e + \frac{1}{e}\right) \quad \text{(v)} \ \frac{1}{2}\left(e - \frac{1}{e}\right).$$

5. Determine the following expansions:

$$\text{(i)} \ 2e^{3x} \quad \text{(ii)} \ 3e^{-2x} \quad \text{(iii)} \ 5e^{-x} \quad \text{(iv)} \ 4\,e^{x/2} \quad \text{(v)} \ e^{-\frac{3x}{2}}$$

as far as the x^5.

6. Find correct to four significant figures, the values of

$$\text{(i)} \quad e^{0.55} \quad \text{(ii)} \ e^{-3.5} \quad \text{(iii)} \ e^{0.02}$$

by considering eight terms.

7. Find the first three terms of the series $\dfrac{e^x - e^{-x}}{e^x}$.

8. How many terms are there in the expansion e^x? is the expansion convergent or divergent? Explain.

9. What is the special property of the exponential function e^x?

10. If x increases how does $y = e^x$ change?

9. GRAPHS OF TRIGONOMETRIC OR CIRCULAR FUNCTIONS OF SINE AND COSINE

Sketches graphs of functions involving sine, cosine.

a. States the approximations $\sin x \approx \tan x \approx x$ and $\cos x \approx 1 - \dfrac{x^2}{2}$ for small x.

b. Sketches graphs of $\sin A$, $\sin 2A$, $2 \sin A$, $\sin A/2$ $\cos A$, $\cos A$, $2 \cos A$, $\cos A$ for values of A 2 between $0°$ and $360°$.

c. Sketches graphs of $\sin^2 A$, $\cos^2 A$, for values of A between $0°$ and $360°$.

d. Sketches graphs of the functions in 9b and 9c where A is replaced by ωt.

e. Defines and identifies amplitude and frequency.

f. Defines angular velocity ω in rad/s and period T as $2\pi/\omega$.

States the approximations $\sin x \approx x$, $\tan x \approx x$ and $\cos x \approx 1 - \dfrac{x^2}{2}$ for small x.

The series expansion for $\sin x$ is given as $\sin x = \dfrac{x}{1!} - \dfrac{x^3}{3!} + \dfrac{x^5}{5!} - \ldots$ where x is expressed in radians. For small values of x, this expansion is approximated $\sin x \approx x$.

We take only the first term as the other terms are extremely small and are negligible.

WORKED EXAMPLE 45

Find the value of $\sin x$ when x

is (i) $1°$ (ii) $0.5°$ (iii) $10^{'}$ (iv) $1^{'}$.

SOLUTION 45

These angles in degrees must be first expressed in radians. If $x°$ is expressed in degrees then x^c in radians is given by $x^c = \dfrac{\pi x}{180}$

(i) $\qquad x^c = \dfrac{\pi}{180}\dfrac{1}{} = 0.0174532^c$

$\sin 0.0174532^c = 0.0174523$

(ii) $\qquad x^c = \dfrac{\pi}{180}\dfrac{1/2}{} = 0.0087266^c$

$\sin 0.0087266^c = 0.0087264892$

(iii) $\qquad x^c = \dfrac{\pi\ {}^{10}\!/_{60}}{180} = 2.9088821 \times 10^{-3}$

$\sin 2.9088821 \text{x} 10^{-3} = 2.908878$

(iv) $\qquad x^c = \dfrac{\pi\ {}^{1}\!/_{60}}{180} = 2.9088821 \times 10^{-4}$

$\sin 2.9088821 \text{x} 10^{-4} = 2.908882 \text{x} 10^{-4}$

This illustrates clearly that if x is very small and it is expressed in radians then $\sin x \approx x$.

similarly $\tan x \approx x$.

The series expansion for cos x is given by cos $\quad x = 1 - \dfrac{x^2}{2} + \dfrac{x^4}{4!} - \dfrac{x^6}{6!} + \ldots$

If x is very small, this can be approximated to cos $\quad x \approx 1 - \dfrac{x^2}{2}$

DEFINES ANGULAR VELOCITY ω IN RADIANS PER SECOND AND PERIOD T AS 2π/ω

ANGULAR VELOCITY

Consider a particle orbiting in a circular path with an angular velocity, ω in radians per second. If the particle turns an angle, θ, as shown in the diagrams and takes t seconds, the angular velocity is given $\omega = \theta/t$.

118

Fig. 50

Some examples possessing angular velocity, wheel of a car rotating a shaft is rotating, a sine wave.

The angle, $\theta = \omega t$, θ is measured in radians, ω in radians per second and t in seconds.

The angular velocity, $\omega = 2\pi f$, where f is the frequency in hertz.

The periodic time, T, is the time taken to trace one complete cycle $\quad T = \dfrac{1}{f} = \dfrac{\omega}{2\pi}$

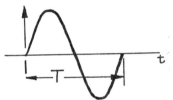

Fig. 51 period or periodic time.

DEFINES AND IDENTIFIES AMPLITUDE AND FREQUENCY

THE FREQUENCY, f, is the number of cycles which are traced in one second

$$f = \frac{1}{T}$$

If $f = 50$ Hz, that is, 50 complete cycles are traced in one second.

TO PLOT GRAPHS OF TRIGONONETRIC FUNCTIONS

A sinewave is represented trigonomentrically by the equation $y = A \sin \omega t$ where A is the amplitude or the maximum or the peak value of the wave, ω is the angular velocity or angular frequency with which the wave displaces and t is the time at any point on the sinewave.

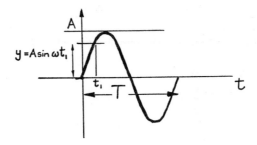

Fig. 52

At $t = t_1, y = A \sin \omega \, t_1$.

Plot the graph $y = 5 \sin 2\pi \, 1000t$ against t, where $t = \Theta / \omega$.

WORKED EXAMPLE 46

Draw the following trigonometric functions:

(i) $y = 2 \sin \omega t$ (ii) $y = 2 \sin (\omega t + \pi/6)$
(iii) $y = 2 \sin (\omega t - \pi/3$

on the same time axis by taking points at intervals of

$\omega t = \pi/6$, displaying $- 2\pi \le \omega t$. (two cycles).

State the amplitude of each waveform, and whether it lags or leads.

Determine the co-ordinates of the points on the y-axis and x-axis where the curves meet and the points of their intersections in the range $(0 \le \omega t \, 2\pi)$.

SOLUTION 46

$\theta^c = \omega t$	0	$\pi/6$	$\pi/3$	$\pi/2$	$2\pi/3$	$5\pi/6$	π
sin ωt	0	0.500	0.866	0.500	0.866	0.500	0
$y = 2$ sin ωt	0	1.000	1.732	1.000	1.732	1.000	0
$y_1 = 2$ sin (ωt + $\pi/6$)	1.000	1.732	2.000	1.732	1.000	0	-1.000
$y_2 = 2$ sin (ωt - $\pi/3$)	-1.732	-2.000	-1.732	-1.000	0	1.000	1.732

$\theta^c = \omega t$	$7\pi/6$	$4\pi/3$	$3\pi/2$	$5\pi/3$	$11\pi/6$	2π	
sin ωt	-0.500	-0.866	-1.000	-0.866	-0.500	0	
$y = 2$ sin ωt	-1.000	-1.732	-2.000	-1.732	-1.000	0	
$y_1 = 2$ sin (ωt + $\pi/6$)	-1.732	-2.000	-1.732	-1.000	0	1.000	
$y_2 = 2$ sin (ωt - $\pi/3$)	2.000	0	-1.000	-1.732	-2.000	-1.732	

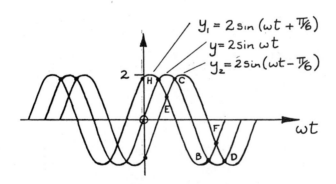

Fig. 53

The amplitude of each waveform is 2.

The sinewave $y = 2 \sin \omega t$ is a reference waveform it begins at the origin, $y = 2 \sin (\omega t + \pi/6)$ leads the wave $y = 2 \sin \omega t$ by $\pi/6$ and $y = 2 \sin (\omega t - \pi/3)$ lags the wave $y = 2 \sin \omega t$ by $\pi/3$.

When $\omega t = 0$ the curves cut the y-axis

$y = 0$ when $\omega t = 0$

$y_1 = 1$ when $\omega t = 0$

$y_2 = -1.732$ when $\omega t = 0$.

When $y = 0$, the curves cut the x-axis from the table, when

$y = 0$, $\omega t = 0, \pi, 2\pi$

$y_1 = 0$, $\omega t = 5\pi/6, 11\pi/6$

$y_2 = 0$, $\omega t = 2\pi/3, 5\pi/3$.

To find the intersections of the sinewaves, we solve the simultaneous equations.

$y = 2 \sin \omega t$

$y_1 = 2 \sin (\omega t + \pi/6)$

when $y = y_1$, $2 \sin \omega t = 2 \sin \omega t \cos \pi/6 + 2 \sin \pi/6 \cos \omega t$

$$2 \sin \omega t = 2 \sin \omega t \quad \frac{\sqrt{3}}{2} + 2\left(\frac{1}{2}\right) \quad \cos \omega t.$$

$$(2 - \sqrt{3}) \sin \omega t = \cos \omega t$$

$$\tan \omega t = \frac{1}{2 - \sqrt{3}}$$

$$\tan \omega t = 3.732$$

$$\omega t = 75° = \frac{5\pi}{12}$$

$$\text{and } \omega t = 255° = \frac{17\pi}{12}.$$

The above curves intersect at $\dfrac{5\pi}{12}$ and $\dfrac{17\pi}{12}$ giving the corresponding values

in y of 1.93 and -1.93. The co-ordinates of intersecting in the range $0 \le \omega t \le 2\pi$

are shown at A $\left(\dfrac{5\pi}{12}, 1.93\right)$ and at B $\left(\dfrac{17\pi}{12}, -1.93\right)$.

The intersections of the two curves $y = 2 \sin \omega t$ and $y_2 = 2 \sin (\omega t - \pi/3)$ are found by solving these equations simultaneously when $y = y_2$

$2 \sin \omega t = 2 \sin (\omega t - \pi/3)$

$2 \sin \omega t = 2 \sin \omega t \cos \pi/3 - 2 \sin \pi/3 \cos \omega t$

$$= 2 (\sin \omega t) \left(\dfrac{1}{2}\right) - 2 \left(\dfrac{\sqrt{3}}{2}\right) \cos \omega t$$

$2 \sin \omega t = \sin \omega t = \sqrt{3} \quad \cos \omega t$

$\sin \omega t = \sqrt{3} \quad \cos \omega t$

$\tan \omega t = - \sqrt{3}$

$\omega t = \dfrac{2\pi}{3}, \dfrac{5\pi}{3}$

The co-ordinates are at $C \left(\dfrac{2\pi}{3}, \sqrt{3}\right)$ and at $D \left(\dfrac{5\pi}{3}, -\sqrt{3}\right)$.

The co-ordinates of the intersections of the curves $y_1 = 2 \sin (\omega t + \pi/6)$ and $y_2 = 2 \sin (\omega t - \pi/3)$. When $y_1 = y_2$, $2 \sin (\omega t + \pi/6) = 2 \sin (\omega t - \pi/3)$ or $\sin \omega t \cos \pi/6 + \sin \pi/6 \cos \omega t = \sin \omega t \cos \pi/3 - \sin \pi/3 \cos \omega t$ or

$\dfrac{\sqrt{3}}{2} \sin \omega t + \dfrac{1}{2} \cos \omega t = \dfrac{1}{2} \sin \omega t - \dfrac{\sqrt{3}}{2} \cos \omega t$

$\left(\dfrac{1}{2} + \dfrac{\sqrt{3}}{2}\right) \cos \omega t = \dfrac{1}{2} \sin \omega t - \dfrac{\sqrt{3}}{2} \sin \omega t$

$\left(\dfrac{1 + \sqrt{3}}{2}\right) \cos \omega t = \dfrac{1 - \sqrt{3}}{2} \sin \omega t$

$$\tan \omega t = \frac{1 + \sqrt{3}}{1 - \sqrt{3}} = \frac{2.732}{-0.732} = -3.7322$$

$$\omega t = 180° - 75° = 105° = \frac{7\pi}{12}$$

$$\text{and } \omega t = 19 \frac{\pi}{12}.$$

The co-ordinates are at $E\left(\frac{7\pi}{12}, 1.93\right)$ and at $F\left(\frac{19\pi}{12}, 1.93\right)$.

Plot on the same graph

(i)   (i) $\sin \frac{1}{2}\omega t$ (ii) $\sin \omega t$ (iii) $\sin 2\omega t$ (iv) $\sin 3\omega t$

$\theta^c = \omega t$	0	$\pi/6$	$\pi/3$	$\pi/2$	$2\pi/3$	π
$\sin \omega t/2$	0	0.259	0.5	0.707	0.866	1
$\sin \omega t$	0	0.5	0.866	1	0.866	0
$\sin 2\omega t$	0	0.866	0.866	0	-0.866	0
$\sin 3\omega t$	0	1	0	1	0	0
$\theta^c = \omega t$	$7\pi/6$	$4\pi/3$	$3\pi/2$	$5\pi/3$	$11\pi/6$	2π
$\sin \omega t/2$	0.966	0.866	0.707	0.5	0.259	0
$\sin \omega t$	-0.5	-0.866	-1	-0.866	-0.5	0
$\sin 2\omega t$	0.866	0.866	0	-0.866	-0.866	0
$\sin 3\omega$	-1	0	1	0	-1	0

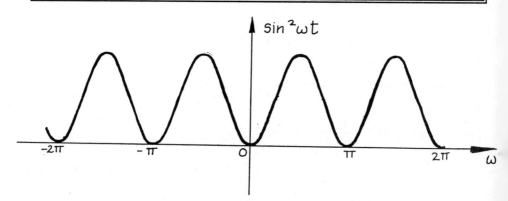

124

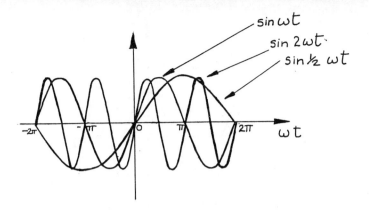

For sin $\dfrac{\omega t}{2}$ half cycle is drawn $0 \le \omega t \le 2\pi$.

For sin ωt full cycle is drawn $0 \le \omega t \le 2\pi$.

For sin $2\,\omega t$ two full cycles are drawn $0 \le \omega t \le 2\pi$.

For sin $3\,\omega t$ three full cycles are drawn $0 \le \omega t \le 2\pi$.

Plot on the same graph

(i) $\cos \dfrac{1}{2} \omega t$ (ii) $\cos \omega t$ (iii) $\cos 2\,\omega t$ (iv) $\cos 3\,\omega t$

For sin $\dfrac{1}{2} \omega t$ half cycle is drawn $0 \le \omega t \le 2\pi$.

For cos ωt full cycle is drawn $0 \le \omega t \le 2\pi$.

For cos $2\,\omega t$ two full cycles is drawn $0 \le \omega t \le 2\pi$.

For cos $3\,\omega t$ three full cycles are drawn $0 \le \omega t \le 2\pi$.

Plot on the same graph

(i) $\cos \dfrac{1}{2} \omega t$ (ii) $\cos \omega t$ (iii) $\cos 2\,\omega t$

(iv) $\cos 3\,\omega t$

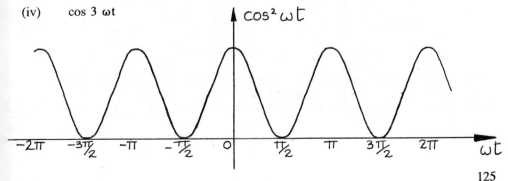

125

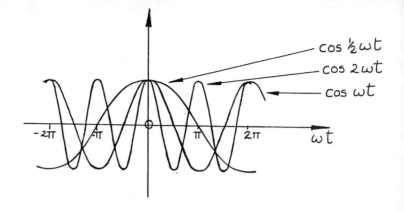

Fig. 54

For sin $\frac{1}{2}\omega t$ half cycle is drawn $0 \le \omega t \le 2\pi$.

For cos ωt full cycle is drawn $0 \le \omega t \le 2\pi$.

For cos 2 ωt two full cycles is drawn $0 \le \omega t \le 2\pi$.

For cos 3 ωt three full cycles are drawn $0 \le \omega t \le 2\pi$.

To plot sin² ωt and cos² ωt for two cycle $-2\pi \le \omega t \le 2\pi$.

The graphs are shown plotted.

$\Theta^c = \omega t$	0	$\pi/6$	$\pi/3$	$\pi/2$	$2\pi/3$	$5\pi/6$
sin ωt	0	0.5	0.866	1	0.866	0.5
sin^2 ωt	0	0.25	0.75	1	0.75	0.25
cos^2 ωt	1	0.75	0.25	0	0.25	0.75

π	$7\pi/6$	$4\pi/3$	$3\pi/2$	$5\pi/3$	$11\pi/6$	2π
0	- 0.5	- 0.866	- 1	- 8.866	- 1.5	0
0	0.25	0.75	1	0.75	0.25	0
0	0.75	0.25	0	0.25	0.75	1

EXERCISES 9

1. Convert the following angles in degrees to the corresponding angles in radians.

   (i) 5° (ii) 2° (iii) 15$^{/}$ (iv) 5$^{/}$ (v) 2$^{/}$

2. Convert the following angles in radians to the corresponding angles in degrees:

   (i) 0.05^c (ii) 0.5^c (iii) 0.00015^c(iv) 1^c.

3. Find the approximate values of the following trigonometric or circular functions:

(i)	sin 1.5$^{/}$	(ii)	sin 0.05^c	(iii)	sin 0.75°
(iv)	tan 0.5°	(v)	cos 1$^{/}$	(vi)	cos 0.75°
(vii)	cos 25$^{/}$.				

4. A sinewave is represented trigonometrically by the equation.

$$y = 30 \sin 31420t$$

   Determine: (i)   the amplitude of the wave
   (ii)   the frequency (Hz)
   (iii)   the period (s)
   (iv)   the angular velocity (rad/s).

5. The angles of a sinewave are given in degrees as 0, 30, 60, 90, 120, 150, 180, 210, 240, 270, 300, 330, 360. Write down the corresponding values of time t, in terms of π and the angular velocity, ω.

6. Sketch the following graphs:-

   (i) sin A (ii) sin $2A$ (iii) 1.5 sin A (iv) sin $A/_2$

   (v) sin² A in the range - $2\pi \le A \le 2\pi$.

7. Sketch the following graphs:-

   (i) cos A (ii) cos $2A$ (iii) 1.5 cos A (iv) cos $A/_2$ (v) cos² A.

8.   Sketch the following graphs against t:

(i) $\sin \omega t$ (ii) $\sin 2\omega t$ (iii) $2 \sin \omega t$

(iv) $\sin \omega t/2$ (v) $\sin^2 \omega t$.

9.   Sketch the following graphs against t:

(i) $\cos \omega t$ (ii) $\cos 2\omega t$ (iii) $2 \cos \omega t$

(iv) $\cos \omega t/2$ (v) $\cos^2 \omega t$.

10.   Sketch the following graphs on the same base for comparison:

(a)   (i) $\sin x$ (ii) $\sin 2x$ (iii) $\sin x/2$

(b)   (i) $\cos x$ (ii) $\cos 2x$ (iii) $\cos x/2$.

10.   RESULTANT OF WAVES

Combines sinewaves.

a.   Determines the single wave resulting from a combination of two waves of the same frequency using phasors and/or a graphical method.

b.   Defines the term phase angle.

c.   Measures the amplitude and phase angle of the resultant wave in 10a.

d.   Determines graphically the single wave resulting from a combination of two waves, within the limitations of 10b and 10c.

e.   Shows that the resultant of two sine waves of different frequencies gives rise to a non-sinusoidal, periodic function.

COMPOUND FORMULAE

$\sin (A + B) = \sin A \cos B + \cos A \sin B$ the expansion of the compound angles.
If $B = - B$

$$\sin (A - B) = \sin A \cos (- B) + \cos A \sin (- B)$$
$$\sin (A - B) = \sin A \cos B - \cos A \sin B$$
$$\cos (- B) = \cos B \text{ even function}$$
$$\sin (- B) = - \sin B \text{ odd function}$$

Fig. 61

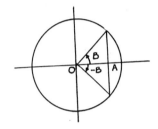

$\cos \quad B = OA$
$\cos (- B) = OA$
therefore $\cos B = \cos (- B)$

EVEN FUNCTION

Fig. 62

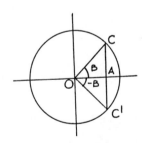

$\sin \quad B = AC$
$\sin (- B) = AC^{\,l}$
but $AC^{\,l} = - AC$
therefore $\sin (- B) = - \sin B$

ODD FUNCTION

$\cos (A + B) = \cos A \cos B - \sin A \sin B$

If $= - B$

$\cos (A - B) = \cos A \cos (- B) - \sin A \sin (- B)$
$\cos (A - B) = \cos A \cos B + \sin A \sin B.$

PHASE ANGLE

The trigonometric or circular function $y = R \sin (\omega t \pm \alpha)$
plot the functions:

If $y = 5 \sin (2\pi 10^3 t + \pi/6)$ and $y = 5 \sin (2\pi\, 10^3\, t - \pi/3)$

where $R = 5$ the amplitude $\omega = 2\pi\, 10^3$ radians, $f = 1000$ Hz
$\alpha = \pi/6$ and $\alpha = -\pi/3$ the phase angles.

When the phase angle is plus the sinewave leads and when the phase angle is minus
the sine wave lags.

Leading waveform means that the peak is reached before and lagging waveform
means that the peak is reached after. This is illustrated.

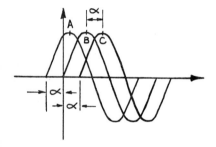

Fig. 63

B is the reference waveform, starts at the origin
C lags B by an angle α
A leads B by an angle α.

Draw the following waveforms:-

$$y_1 = 3 \sin\ \omega t$$
$$y_2 = 5 \sin (\omega t + \pi/6)$$
$$y_3 = 4 \sin (\omega t - \pi/3)$$

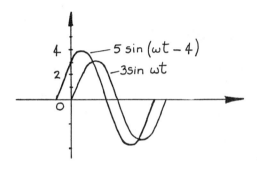

Fig. 64

PHASE ANGLE LEADING AND LAGGING

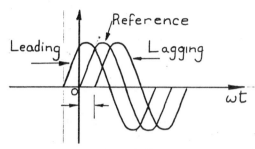

Fig. 65

Reference waveform $y = R \sin \omega t$

Leading the reference waveform

$$y = R \sin (\omega t + \alpha)$$

Lagging the reference waveform

$$y = R \sin (\omega t - \alpha).$$

$R \sin (\omega t + \alpha)$ to be expressed in the form $a \cos \omega t + b \sin \omega t$.

Using $\sin (A + B) = \sin A \cos B + \cos A \sin B$, we expand $R \sin (\omega t + \alpha)$
$= R \sin \omega t \cos \alpha + R \sin \alpha \cos \omega t$.

WORKED EXAMPLE 47

Express $3 \sin (\omega t + \pi/3)$ in the form $a \cos \omega t + b \sin \omega t$

SOLUTION 47

$$3 \sin (\omega t + \pi/3) = 3 \sin \omega t \cos \pi/3 + 3 \sin \pi/3 \cos \omega t$$

$$= \sin \omega t + 3 \frac{\sqrt{3}}{2} \cos \omega t.$$

WORKED EXAMPLE 48

To express $\dfrac{3}{2} \sin \omega t + \dfrac{3 \sqrt{3}}{2} \cos \omega t$ in the form $R \sin (\omega t + \alpha)$.

SOLUTION 48

$$\frac{3}{2} \sin \omega t + \frac{3 \sqrt{3}}{2} \cos \omega t \equiv R \sin \omega t \cos \alpha + R \sin \alpha \cos \omega t.$$

Equating the coefficients of $\sin \omega t$, we have $R \cos \alpha = 3/2$ hence $\cos \alpha = \dfrac{3/2}{R}$.

Equating the coefficents of $\cos \omega t$, we have $R \sin \alpha = \dfrac{3 \sqrt{3}}{2}$

hence $\sin \alpha = \dfrac{3 \frac{\sqrt{3}}{2}}{R}$.

Forming a right angled triangle

$$\tan \alpha = \frac{3 \frac{\sqrt{3}}{2}}{\frac{3}{2}} = \sqrt{3}$$

$$\alpha = \pi/3$$

$$R^2 = \left(\frac{3}{2}\right)^2 + \left(\frac{3 \sqrt{3}}{2}\right)^2 = \frac{9}{4} + \frac{27}{4} = \frac{36}{4}$$

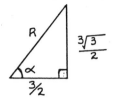

Fig. 66

$$R^2 = 9 \quad \text{and} \quad \boxed{R = 3}$$

$\alpha \cos \omega t + b \sin \omega t = R \sin (\omega t \pm \alpha)$
$$= R \sin \omega t \cos \alpha + R \sin \alpha \cos \omega t$$

$a = R \sin \alpha$
$b = R \cos \alpha \quad a^2 + b^2 = R^2 \quad \tan \alpha = a/b$

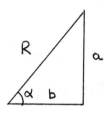

Fig. 67

ALTERNATING VOLTAGES AND CURRENTS

Alternating voltages and currents can be expressed trigonometrically.

WORKED EXAMPLE 49

An alternating voltage is given by the expression

$$v = 100 \sin (3142t + \pi/3).$$

Draw the above waveforms for two cycles.

Calculate: (i)   the peak value of the voltage
          (ii)   the freqnency
          (iii)   the angular velocity
          (iv)   the periodic time
          (v)   the instantaneous value of the voltage
                 when $t = 0.5$ ms.

SOLUTION 49

The waveform is plotted as shown in the diagram of **Fig.**

(i)   Peak value of the voltage = 100 volts.

(ii) $\omega = 2\pi f = 3142$
       $f = 500$ Hz

(iii) $\omega = 3142$ radians/second

(iv) $T = \dfrac{1}{f} = \dfrac{1}{500} = 2$ ms

(v) $v = 100 \sin (3142 \times 0.5 \times 10^{-3} + \pi/3)$
       $= 100 \sin (2.6181976^{c)}$
       $= 50$ volts.

The total angle $3142t + \pi/3$ should be expressed in radians.

WORKED EXAMPLE 50

An instantaneous current is given by the expression

$$i = 50 \sin (3142t - \pi/6) \text{ mA}$$

Calculate: (i)   the frequency
            (ii)   the amplitude
            (iii)   the instantaneous value after 0.1 ms.

SOLUTION 50

(i) $\omega = 2\pi f = 3142$

$$f = \frac{3142}{2\pi} = 500 \text{ Hz}$$

(ii)   50 mA

(iii) $i = 50 \sin (3142 \times 0.1 \times 10^{-3} - \pi/6)^c$ mA
          $= 50 [-0.2093987]\text{mA}$
          $= 10.5$ mA.

WORKED EXAMPLE 51

A sinusoidal alternating voltage has the equation
          $v = 141.4 \sin (377t + \pi/2)$ volts.

Determine   (i)   the peak value
                  (ii)   the angular velocity
                  (iii)   the periodic time
                  (iv)   the frequency
                  (v)   the instantaneous voltage
                           when $t = 2.5$ ms.

SOLUTION 51

          (i)   141.4 volts

          (ii) $\omega = 377$ radians/second

          (iii) $T = \dfrac{1}{f} = \dfrac{1}{60} = 0.0167 \text{s} = 16.7 \text{ ms}$

          (iv) $2\pi f = 377$
                   $f = 60 \text{ Hz}$

WORKED EXAMPLE 52

The voltages across three components in a circuit can be expressed as:

$v_1 = 35 \sin \omega t$, $v_2 = 50 \sin (\omega t + \pi/3)$, $v_3 = 10 \sin (\omega t - \pi/2)$.

Determine the resultant total voltage across the circuit and express it in the form

$$v_R = v_m \sin (\omega t \pm \theta).$$

SOLUTION 52

$v = 35 \sin \omega t + 50 \sin (\omega t + \pi/3) + 70 \sin (\omega t - \pi/2)$

$v = 35 \sin \omega t + 50 \sin \omega t \cos \pi/3 \; 50 \sin \pi/3 \; \cos \omega t$

$\quad + 70 \sin \omega t \cos \pi/2 - 70 \sin \pi/2 \; \omega t$

$v = 35 \sin \omega t + 50 \sin \omega t \left(\dfrac{1}{2}\right) + 50 \dfrac{\sqrt{3}}{2} \cos \omega t + 70 \sin \omega t \,(0)$

$- 70 \cos \omega t$

$v = 35 \sin \omega t + 25 \sin \omega t + 25 \sqrt{3} \; \cos \omega t - 70 \cos \omega t$

$v = 60 \sin \omega t - 26.7 \cos \omega t = R \sin (\omega t - \alpha)$

$v = 60 \sin \omega t - 26.7 \cos \omega t \equiv R \sin \omega t \cos \alpha - R \sin \alpha \cos \omega t$

The coefficients of sin ωt are equal

$\quad 60 = R \cos \alpha \; ...(1)$

The coefficients of cos ωt are equal $- 26.7 = - R \sin \alpha \; ...(2)$

From (1) $\cos \alpha = 60/R$

From (2) $\sin \alpha = 26.7/R$

Constructing a right angled triangle

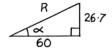

Fig. 68

$R^2 = 60^2 + 26.7^2 = 4312.89$

$R = 65.7$

$\tan \alpha = \dfrac{26.7}{60}$ or $\alpha = 23^0 \, 59' = 0.4186\,881^c \approx 0.42^c$

$$V_R = 65.7 \sin(\omega t) - 0.42^c)$$

Adding two sine waves of the same frequency

The following examples will illustrate the effect.

(a)   If $y_1 = 3 \sin \omega t$

$y_2 = 4 \sin \omega t$

The resultant $y = y_1 + y_2 = 3 \sin \omega t + 4 \sin \omega t = 7 \sin \omega t$.

The resultant sinewave is another sinewave with different amplitude.

(b)   If $y_1 = 3 \sin \omega t$

$$y_2 = 4 \sin(\omega t + \pi/3)$$

$y = y_1 + y_2 = 3 \sin \omega t + 4 \sin(\omega t + \pi/3)$

$= 3 \sin \omega t + 4 \sin \omega t \cos \pi/3 + 4 \sin \pi/3 \cos \omega t$

$= 3 \sin \omega t + 2 \sin \omega t + 2\sqrt{3} \cos \omega t$

$= 5 \sin \omega t + 2\sqrt{3} \cos \omega t$

$= R \sin(\omega t + \alpha)$

$= R \sin \omega t \cos \alpha R \sin \alpha \cos \omega t$

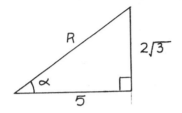

Fig. 69

$5 = R \cos \alpha$ and $R \sin \alpha = 2\sqrt{3}$

$$\left(2\sqrt{3}\right)^2 + 5^2 \; R = \sqrt{25} \quad 25 + 12 = \sqrt{37}$$

$$\tan \alpha = 2\sqrt{\frac{3}{5}} \quad \alpha = \tan^{-1} 2\sqrt{3/5} = 34.72°$$

$$y = \sqrt{37} \; \sin(\omega t + 34.72°)$$

the amplitude is different to the other amplitudes and the sinewave is leading the individual sinewaves by an angle of 34.72°.

Therefore adding sinewaves or cosine waves of the same frequency, the resultant is a sinewave which is displaced by an angle α either leading or lagging of different amplitudes.

Adding two sinewaves of different frequency

$$y_1 = \sin \omega t$$

$$y_2 = 4 \sin 2 \omega t$$

The resultant $y = y_1 + y_2 = 3 \sin \omega t + 4 \sin 2 \omega t$

$$= 3 \sin \omega t + 8 \sin \omega t \cos \omega t$$

which is a non-sinusoidal waveform which is called complex waveform.

$y = \sin \omega t + \dfrac{1}{2} \sin 2\ \omega t$ gives the waveform

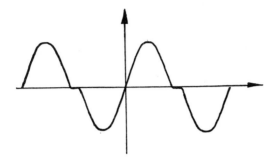

Fig. 70   **Complex Wave**

The resultant of the waveforms

$y = 0.5 \sin x + 0.5 \sin 2x + 0.5 \sin 3x$

is shown in the graph.

EXERCISES 10

1.   Sketch $y = 3 \sin x$ and $y = 4 \sin x$
     and hence obtain $y_1 + y_2$.

2.   Sketch $y_1 = 2 \sin 2x$ and $y_2 = \sin (2x + \pi/3)$ and hence combine the
     waveforms.

3.   Find the resultant waveform

     $y = 2 \sin x + 3 \sin 2x$.

4.   Find the resultant curve

     $y = \sin \theta/2 + \sin \theta + \sin 2\theta$.

5.   Write down the equation of two waveforms, one has amplitude 5 and leads
     by 30° and the other has amplitude 12 and lag by 90°.

PART II

SOLUTIONS 1

1.　　(i)　　$\log_e 1.234 = 0.21$

　　　(ii)　　$\log_e 12.34 = 2.51$

　　　(iii)　　$\log_e 1234 = 7.12$
　　　　　　in three significant figures

2.　　(i)　　$\log_e N = 4.174$

　　　　　　$e^{4.174} = N = 64.98$

　　　(ii)　　$\log_e N = 9.21$

　　　　　　$e^{9.21} = N = 9997$

　　　(iii)　　$\log_e N = -3.66$

　　　　　　$e^{-3.66} = N = 0.0257$

　　　　　　in four significant figures

3.　　　　　$N = No\ e^{-\lambda t}$

　　　　　when $t = 1500$ years

　　　　　　　$\frac{1}{2} No = No\ e^{-\lambda 1500}$

　　　　　　　$\frac{1}{2} = e^{-1500\lambda}$

　　　　　$e^{1500\lambda} = 2$

taking logarithms to the base e on both sides

　　　　　　$\ln e^{1500\lambda} = \ln 2$

$$1500 \; \lambda \; \ln e = \ln 2$$

$$\lambda = \frac{\ln 2}{1500} = 4.621 \times 10^{-4}$$

$$\frac{1}{20} \; No = No \; e^{-4.621 \times 10^4 t}$$

$$\frac{1}{20} = e^{-4.621 \times 10^{-4} t}$$

$$20 = e^{4.621 \times 10^{-4} t}$$

$$\ln 20 = 4.621 \times 10^{-4} \; t \ln e$$

$$t = \frac{\ln 20}{4.621 \times 10^{-4}}$$

$$\tau = 6483 \text{ years.}$$

4. $e^{2x} - 5 \; e^x + 6 = 0 \; ...(1)$

$y = e^x$ squaring both sides $y^2 = (e^x)^2$ or

$y^2 = e^{2x}$ since $(e^x)(e^x) = e^{2x}$.

Equation (1) is now written in terms of y

$y^2 - 5y + 6 = 0$

$$y = \frac{5 \pm \sqrt{25 - 24}}{2} = \frac{5 \pm 1}{2}$$

$$y = \frac{5 + 1}{2} \quad \text{and} \quad y = \frac{5 - 1}{2}$$

$y = 3$ and $y = 2$

therefore $e^x = 3$, to find x, we must take logs to the base e on both sides

$$\ln e^x = \ln 3$$

$$x \ln e = \ln 3$$

$$x = \ln 3$$

$$x = 1.0986123$$

$$x \approx 1.099$$

also $e^x = 2$

$$\ln e^x = 2$$

$$x = \ln 2$$

$$x = 0.693.$$

Therefore the solutions of equation (1) are $x = 0.693$ and 1.099.

5.　　　　　$6\,e^{2x} - 7\,e^x + 2 = 0$

Let $W = e^x$ then $e^{2x} = W^2$

$$6\,W^2 - 7W + 2 = 0$$

$$W = \frac{7 \pm \sqrt{49 - 4 \times 6 \times 2}}{12} = \frac{7 \pm \sqrt{49 - 48}}{12} = \frac{7 \pm 1}{12}$$

$$W = 2/3 \ \text{or} \ W = 1/2$$

$$e^x = 2/3 \ \text{or} \ e^x = 1/2$$

taking logs

$$\ln e^x = \ln 2/3 \qquad\qquad \ln e^x = \ln 1/2$$

$$x = \ln 2/3 \qquad\qquad x = \ln 1/2$$

$$x = -0.405 \qquad\qquad x = -0.693.$$

SOLUTIONS 2

1.   (i) $\sqrt{-2} = \sqrt{(-1)(2)} = \sqrt{-1}\sqrt{2} = j\sqrt{2}$

     (ii) $\sqrt{-4} = \sqrt{(-1)(4)} = \sqrt{-1}\sqrt{4} = j\,2$

     (iii) $\sqrt{-8} = \sqrt{(-1)(8} = \sqrt{(-1)}\sqrt{8} = j\sqrt{8} = j\,2\sqrt{2}$

     (iv) $\sqrt{-16} = \sqrt{(-1)(16)} = \sqrt{-1}\sqrt{16} = j\,4$

     (v) $\sqrt{-27} = \sqrt{(-1)(27)} = \sqrt{-1}\sqrt{27} = j\,3\sqrt{3}$

2.   (i) $3x^2 - x + 1 = 0$ using $\;x = -\dfrac{b \pm \sqrt{b^2 - 4ac}}{2a}$

$$x = \frac{-(-1) \pm \sqrt{(-1)^2 - 4(3)(1)}}{2 \times 3} = \frac{1 \pm \sqrt{1 - 12}}{6} = \frac{1 \pm \sqrt{-11}}{6}$$

$$x = \frac{1}{6} \pm j\,\frac{\sqrt{11}}{6} \qquad \text{complex roots.}$$

     (ii) $x^2 - 4x + 8 = 0$ using the quadratic formula

$$x = -\frac{(-4) \pm \sqrt{(-4)^2 - 4 \times 1 \times 8}}{2 \times 1} = \frac{4 \pm \sqrt{16 - 32}}{2} = \frac{4 \pm \sqrt{-}}{2}$$

$x = 2 \pm j2$ complex roots

     (iii) $x^2 + 2x + 2 = 0$ using the quadratic formula

$$x = \frac{-2 \pm \sqrt{2^2 - 4 \times 1 \times 2}}{2} = \frac{-2 \pm \sqrt{4 - 8}}{2} = \frac{2}{2} \pm \frac{\sqrt{-4}}{2}$$

$x = -1 \pm j1$ complex roots

     (iv) $-5x^2 + 7x + 5 = 0$ using the quadratic formula

$$x = \frac{-7 \pm \sqrt{7^2 - 4(-5)(5)}}{2 \times (-5)} = \frac{-7 \pm \sqrt{49 + 100}}{-10} = \frac{-7 \pm \sqrt{149}}{-10}$$

$$x = \frac{-7}{-10} \pm \frac{\sqrt{149}}{-10} = \frac{7}{10} \pm \frac{12.2}{-10} = 0.7 \mp 1.22 \quad \text{real roots.}$$

(v)　　$-x^2 + x - 5 = 0$ using the quadratic formula

$$x = \frac{-1 \pm \sqrt{1 - 4(-1)(-5)}}{2 \times (-1)} = \frac{-1 \pm \sqrt{1 - 20}}{-2} = \frac{-1 \pm \sqrt{-19}}{-2}$$

$$x = \frac{-1}{-2} \pm j \frac{4.36}{-2}$$

$x = 0.5 \mp j2.18$ complex roots.

3.　　(i)　　$A\ (1,3)$,　$x = 1$ and $y = 3$ then $Z_A = 1 + j3$

　　(ii)　　$E\ (-1,3)$,　$x = -1$ and $y = 3$ then $Z_E = -1 + j3$

　　(iii)　　$F\ (2, -4)$, $x = 2$ and $y = -4$ then $Z_F = 2 - j4$

　　(iv)　　$J\ (-3,-4)$,　$x = -3$ and $y = -4$ then $Z_J = -3 - j4$

　　　　　　where $Z = x + jy$.

4.　　(i)　　$Z_1 = 3 + j4$,　　　$P_1\ (3,\ 4)$

　　(ii)　　$Z_2 = 3 - j4$,　　　$P_2\ (3, -4)$

　　(iii)　　$Z_3 = -3 + j4$,　　　$P_3\ (3,\ 4)$

　　(iv)　　$Z_4 = -3 + -j4$,　　　$P_4\ (-3,\ -4)$.

5.

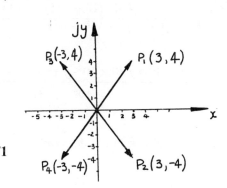

Fig. 71

145

6.   (i)   Re $Z = x$ and Im $Z = y$, then $Z = x + jy$

       (ii)   Re $Z = -3$ and Im $Z = 5$, then $Z = -3 + j5$.

7. $E_1 = 20 + j30$ and $E_2 = 10 + j15$

       $E_1 + E_2 = (20 + j30) + (10 + j15) = (20 + 10) + j(30 + 15)$

       $E_1 + E_2 = 30 + j45$

                add the real terms separately and
                add the imaginary terms separately

       $E1 - E_2 = (20 + j30) - (10 + j15) = 20 + j30 - 10 -j15$

                $= (20 - 10) + j(30 - 15) = 10 + j15$

       $E_1 - E_2 = 10 + j15$.

(b) $E_1 \ E_2 = (20 + j30)(10 + j15) = 20 \times 10 + 20\,j15 +$

                $+ j30 \times 10 + j30 \times j15 = 200 + j300 + j300$

                $+ j^2\,450$

                $= (200 - 450) + j600 = -250 + j600$.

Multiplying numerator and denominator by the conjugate of the denominator of the denominator.

$$\frac{E_1}{E_2} = \frac{20 + j\,30}{10 + j\,15} = \frac{20 + j\,30}{10 + j\,15} \times \frac{10 - j\,15}{10 - j\,15}$$

$$\frac{E_1}{E_2} = \frac{(20 + j\,30)(10 - j\,15)}{(10 + j\,15)(10 - j\,15} = \frac{20 \times 10 + j\,30 \times 10 - j15 \times 20 + j\,30 \times (-j15)}{10^2 - j^2 15^2}$$

$$= \frac{20 \times 10 + j\,30 \times 10 - j\,15 \times 20 + j\,30 \times (-j\,15}{10^2 - j^2\,15^2}$$

remember $(a + b)(a - b) = (a^2 - b^2)$

$$= \frac{200 + j\,300 - j\,300 - j^2\,450}{100 - (-1)\,225} = \frac{650}{100 + 225}$$

$$= \frac{650}{325} = 2.$$

8.   (i) $(3\,j)\,(5\,j) = 15\,j^2 = -15 = -15 + j\,0$

      (ii) $(4 - 5\,j)\,(1 + j) = 4 - 5\,j + 4\,j - 5\,j^2 = 4 + 5 - j = 9 - j$

      (iii) $(1 + j)\,(1 - j) = 1^2 - j^2 = 1 + 1 = 2$

      (iv) $(4 + 3\,j)^2 = 4^2 + (3\,j)^2 + 2\,(4)\,(3\,j) = 16 + 9\,j^2 + 24\,j$

               $= 16 - 9 + 24\,j = 7 + 24\,j$

      (v) $(1 - i^2)^2 = 1^2 + (-i^2)^2 + 2\,(1)\,(-i^2) = 1 + \left[-(-1)\right]^2 + 2\,(-(-1))$

               $= 1 + 1 + 2 = 4.$

9.   (i) $Z_1\,Z_2 = (3 - 4j)\,(1 + j) = 3 - 4j + 3j - 4j^2 = 3 + 4 - j = 7 - j$

      (ii) $Z_1\,Z_3 = (3 - 4\,j)\,(2 + 3\,j) = 6 - 8\,j + 9\,j - 12\,j^2 = 6 + 12 + j = 18 + j$

      (iii) $Z_1\,Z_2\,Z_3 = (3 - 4j)\,(1 + j)\,(2 + 3j) = (7 - j)\,(2 + j3) = 14 - 2j + j21 - j$

               $= 14 + 3 + 19j = 17 + 19j.$

10.   (i) $ZZ^* = (x + jy)\,(x - jy) = (x^2 - j^2\,y^2) = x^2 + y^2$

      (ii) $\left(\dfrac{1}{Z}\right)^* = \left(\dfrac{1}{x + jy}\right)^* = \left(\dfrac{x - jy}{(x + jy)(x - jy)}\right)^* = \left(\dfrac{x - jy}{x^2 + y^2}\right)^* = \dfrac{x}{x^2 + y^2} + j\,\dfrac{y}{x^2 + y}$

$$\frac{1}{Z^*} = \frac{1}{x - jy} \times \frac{x + jy}{x + jy} = \frac{x + jy}{x^2 + y^2} = \frac{x}{x^2 + y^2} + j\,\frac{y}{x^2 + y^2}$$

      therefore $\left(\dfrac{1}{Z}\right)^* = \dfrac{1}{Z^*}.$

SOLUTIONS 3

1.   (i) $Z_1 = 1 + j\sqrt{3}$

$$\left|Z_1\right| = \sqrt{1^2 + \left(\sqrt{3}\right)^2} = \sqrt{1 + 3} = 2 \qquad \arg Z_1 = \tan^{-1} \frac{\sqrt{3}}{1}$$

    (ii) $Z_2 = \sqrt{2} - j$

$$\left|Z_2\right| = \sqrt{(2)^2 + (-1)^2} = \sqrt{2 + 1} = \sqrt{3} \quad \arg Z_2 = -\tan^{-1} \frac{1}{\sqrt{2}}$$

    (iii) $Z_3 = 1 + j\sqrt{3}$

$$\left|Z_4\right| = \sqrt{(-1)^2 + \left(\sqrt{3}\right)^2} = \sqrt{1 + 3} = 2 \qquad \arg Z_3 = 180° - \tan_{-1}$$

    (iv) $Z_5 = 2 + j\,3$

$$\left|Z_4\right| \quad \sqrt{(2)^2 + (3)^2} = \sqrt{4 + 9} = \sqrt{13} \qquad \arg Z_4 = \tan^{-1} \frac{3}{2}$$

    (v) $Z_5 = -2 - 4j$

$$\left|Z_5\right| = \sqrt{(-2)^2 + (-4)^2} = 4 + 16 = 4.47 \, \arg Z_5 = -\left[180° - \tan^{-}\right.$$

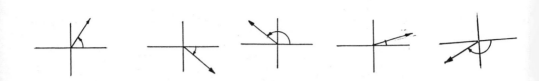

Fig. 72 (i)   **Fig. 73 (ii)**   **Fig. 74 (iii)**   **Fig. 75 (iv)**   **Fig. 76 (v)**

2.   (i) $Z_1 = 3 + 4j$ $\left|Z_1\right| = \sqrt{(3)^2 + (4)^2} = \sqrt{9 + 16} = \sqrt{25} = 5$

$$\arg Z_1 = \tan^{-1} 4/3 = \Theta = 53.13°$$

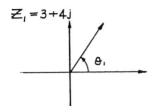

Fig. 77

(ii) $Z_2 = 3 - 4j$ $\left| Z_2 \right| = \sqrt{(3)^2 + (-4^2)} = \sqrt{9 + 16} = \sqrt{25} = 5$

$$\arg Z_2 = \tan^{-1} 4/3 = -\Theta_2 = -53.13°$$

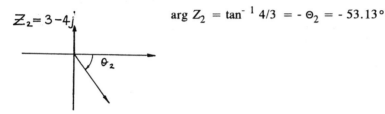

Fig. 78

(iii) $Z_3 = 3 + 4j$ $\left| Z_3 \right| = \sqrt{(-3)^2 + (4)^2} = \sqrt{9 + 16} = \sqrt{25} = 5$

$$\arg Z = [180° - 53.13°] = -126.87°$$

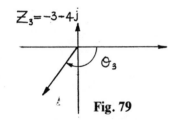

Fig. 79

(iv) $Z_4 = -3 + 4j$

$$\left| Z_4 \right| = \sqrt{(-3)^2 + (4)^2} = \sqrt{9 + 16} = \sqrt{25} = 5$$

$$\arg Z_4 = 180° - \tan^{-1} \frac{4}{3}$$

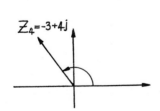

Fig. 80 $= 126.87°$

3.   (i) $Z_1 = 3 \,\underline{/\,-30°}$

$= (\cos 30° - j \sin 30°) = 3\,(0.866 - j\,0.5)$

$Z_1 = 2.598 - j\,1.5$

(ii) $Z_2 = 5 \,\underline{/\,-\pi/2} = 5\,(\cos \pi/2 - j \sin \pi/2) = 5\,(0 - j1)$

$Z_2 = -j5$

(iii) $Z_3 = 1 \,\underline{/\,-180°} = 1\,(\cos 180° - j \sin 180°) = 1(-1 - j0)$

$Z_3 = -1$

(iv) $Z_4 = 7 \,\underline{/\,4\pi/3} = 7\,(\cos 4\pi/3 + j \sin 4\pi/3)$

$Z_4 = 7\,(-0.5 - j0.866) = -3.5 - j6.062$

$Z_4 = -3.5 - j6.062$

(v) $Z_5 = 3 \,\underline{/\,360°}$

$= 3\,(\cos 360° + j \sin 360°)$

$= 3\,(1 + j0) = 3$

5. $|Z| = \sqrt{2}$ and arg $Z = \pi/3$

(i) $Z = \sqrt{2} \,\underline{/\,\pi/3} = \sqrt{2}\,(\cos \pi/3 + j \sin \pi/3)$

$Z = \sqrt{2}\,(0.5 + j\,0.866)$

$Z = 0.707 + j1.225$

(ii) $Z = \sqrt{2} \,\underline{/\,\pi/3} = \sqrt{2}$

$(\cos \pi/3 + j \sin \pi/3)$

6.

(a)

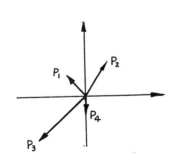

$$Z_1 = -1 - j \qquad Z_2 = 1 + j\sqrt{3}$$

$$Z_1 - Z_2 = -1 - j - 1 - j\sqrt{3} = -2 - j\,2.732$$

$$Z_1 - Z_2 = -2 - j\,2.732$$

$$Z_1 + Z_2 = -1 - j + 1 + j\sqrt{3} = j\,0.732$$

Fig. 81

(b)   (i) $Z_1 = -1 - j \left| Z_1 \right| = \sqrt{(-1)^2 + (1)^2} = \sqrt{1 + 1} = \sqrt{2}$

$$\arg Z_1 = 180° + \tan^{-1} 1$$

$$= 180° + 45°$$

$$= 225° = \theta$$

Fig. 82

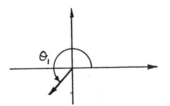

(ii) $Z_2 = 1 + j\sqrt{3}$

$$\left| Z_2 \right| = \sqrt{1 + \left(\sqrt{3}\right)^2} = \sqrt{4} = 2$$

$$\arg Z_2 = \tan^{-1} \frac{\sqrt{3}}{1} = \theta_2 = 60°$$

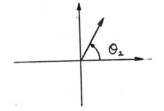

Fig. 83

151

(iii) $\quad Z_1 Z_2 = \sqrt{2}\ \underline{/\ 225°} \cdot 2\ \underline{/\ 60°} = 2\sqrt{2}\ \underline{/\ 285°}$

$$\left| Z_1 Z_2 \right| = 2\sqrt{2}$$

$$\arg Z_1 Z_2 = 285°$$

(iv) $\quad \dfrac{Z_1}{Z_2} = \dfrac{\sqrt{2}\ \underline{/\ 225°}}{2\ \underline{/\ 60°}} = \dfrac{\sqrt{2}}{2}\ \underline{/\ 165°}$

$$\left| \dfrac{Z_1}{Z_2} \right| = \dfrac{\sqrt{2}}{2} \qquad \arg \dfrac{Z_1}{Z_2} = 165°$$

(v) $\quad \dfrac{Z_2}{Z_1} = \dfrac{2\ \underline{/\ 60°}}{\sqrt{2}\ \underline{/\ 225°}} = \dfrac{2}{\sqrt{2}}\ \underline{/\ -165°}$

$$\arg \dfrac{Z_2}{Z_1} = -165° \qquad \left| \dfrac{Z_2}{Z_1} \right| = 2\sqrt{2}\ \dfrac{\sqrt{2}}{\sqrt{2}} = \sqrt{2}$$

7. $\qquad Z_1 = 5\ \underline{/\ 30°}, \quad Z_2 = 7\ \underline{/\ 50°}, \quad Z_3 = 9\ \underline{/\ -45°}$

(i) $\quad Z_1 Z_2 Z_3 = 5\ \underline{/\ 30°}\ 7\ \underline{/\ 50°}\ 9\ \underline{/\ -45°} = 315\ \underline{/\ 30°+50°-45°}$

$$Z_1 Z_2 Z_3 = 315\ \underline{/\ 35°}$$

(ii) $\quad Z_1 Z_2 = 5\ \underline{/\ 30°}\ 7\ \underline{/\ 50°} = 35\ \underline{/30° + 50°} = 35\ \underline{/\ 80°}$

(iii) $\quad Z_3 Z_1 = 9\ \underline{/\ -45°}\ 5\ \underline{/30°} = 45\ \underline{/\ -15°}$

(iv) $\quad \dfrac{Z_1}{Z_3} = \dfrac{7\ \underline{/\ 50°}}{9\ \underline{/\ -45°}} = 0.778\ \underline{/\ 95°}$

(v) $\quad Z_1 Z_2 \Big/ Z_3 = 35\ \underline{/\ 80°} \Big/ 9\ \underline{/\ -45°} = \dfrac{35}{9}\ \underline{/\ 80° - (45°)} = 3.89\ \underline{/\ 12}$

The cartesian form

(i) $Z_1 Z_2 Z_3 = 315\,\underline{/\ 35°} = 315\,(\cos 35° + j \sin 35°)$

       $Z_1 Z_2 Z_3 = (0.819 + j\,0.574) = 258 + j\,181$

(ii) $Z_1 Z_2 = 35\,\underline{/\ 80°} = 35\,(\cos 80° + j \sin 80°) = 35\,(0.174 + j\,0.985)$

       $Z_1 Z_2 = 6.09 + j\,34.5$

(iii) $Z_3 Z_1 = 45\,\underline{/\ \text{-}15°} = 45\,(\cos 15° - j \sin 15°)$

          $= 45\,(0.966 - j\,0.259)$

       $Z_3 Z_1 = 43.5 - j\,11.7$

(iv) $\dfrac{Z_2}{Z_3} = 0.778\,\underline{/\ 95°} = 0.778\;(\cos 95° + j \sin 95°)$

          $= 0.778\,(- 0.0872 + j\,0.996)$

          $= - 0.0678 + j\,0.775$

(v) $\dfrac{Z_1 Z_2}{Z_3} = 3.89\,\underline{/\ 125°} = 3.89\;(\cos 125° + j \sin 125°)$

             $= 3.89\,(-0.574 + j\,0.189)$

             $= -2.23 + j\,3.19.$

8.   (i) $\sqrt{j} = \pm\,(a + jb)$ squaring up both sides where a and b are real
             numbers $j = a^2 + j^2 b^2 + j2\,ab = a^2 - b^2 + j2\,ab$ equating real
             and imaginary terms $0 = a^2 - b^2$ or $a^2 = b^2$ or $a = \pm\,b$
             $1 = 2ab$, if $a = b$, $1 = 2a^2$ or $\alpha = \pm\ 1\sqrt{2}$

             if $a = -b$, $1 = 2ab = -2\,b^2$ $b = \pm\left(-\dfrac{1}{2}\right)$

             which are complex numbers and are disregarded.

             Therefore $\sqrt{j} = \pm\,(a + ja) = \pm\,a\,(1 + j) = \mp\dfrac{1}{\sqrt{2}}\,(1 + j$ that

             is the square roots of $\sqrt{j}$ are $\dfrac{1}{\sqrt{2}} + \dfrac{1}{\sqrt{2}}\,j$ and $-\dfrac{1}{\sqrt{2}} - \dfrac{1}{\sqrt{2}}j.$

(ii) Let $\sqrt{3 - j4} = \pm (a + jb)$ squaring up both sides

$3 - j4 = (a^2 + j^2 b^2 + j2ab) = a^2 - b^2 + j2ab$ equating
real and imaginary terms $3 = a^2 - b^2$ and $- 4 = 2ab$ or $a = -\dfrac{2}{b}$

$3 = \left(-\dfrac{2}{b}\right)^2 - b^2 = \dfrac{4}{b^2} - b^2$ multiplying each term by b^2

$3b^2 = 4 - b^4$ or $b^4 + 3b^2 - 4 = 0$.

Let $b^2 = W$

$W^2 + 3W - 4 = 0$ applying the quadratic formula

$$W = \frac{- 3 \pm \sqrt{9 - 4\,(1) \times (- 4)}}{2} = \frac{- 3 \pm \sqrt{9 + 16}}{2} = -\frac{3 \pm 5}{2}$$

$$W = 1 \text{ or } W = - 4$$

$$b^2 = 1 \text{ or } b = \pm 1$$

$a = -\dfrac{2}{b} = -\dfrac{2}{1}$ or $a = -\dfrac{2}{- 1} = 2$

$a = - 2$ when $b = 1$ and $a = 2$ when $b = -1$

therefore $\sqrt{3 - j4} = \pm (-2 + j)$
the square roots of $3 - j4$ are $- 2 + j$, and $2 - j$.

(iii) $\sqrt{i - 2} = \pm (1 + jb)$ squaring up both sides

$i - 2 = a^2 - b^2 + j2ab$ equating real and imaginary
terms $a^2 - b^2 = - 2$ and $1 = 2ab$ or $a = 1/2b$.

$\left(\dfrac{1}{2b}\right)^2 - b^2 = - 2$ or $\dfrac{1}{4 b^2} - b^2 = -2$ multiplying each term by

$b^2, \dfrac{1}{4} - b^4 = -2 b^2$ or $b^4 - 2 b^2 - \dfrac{1}{4} = 0$ $4 b^4 - 8 b^2 - 1 = 0$

applying the quadratic formula $b^2 = \dfrac{8 \pm \sqrt{64 + 4 \times 4}}{2 \times 4}$

$b^2 = \dfrac{8 \pm \sqrt{16 \times 5}}{8} = \dfrac{8 \pm 4\sqrt{5}}{8} = 1 \pm \dfrac{1}{2}\sqrt{5}$

$b^2 = 1 \pm 1.118034$ which is $b^2 = 2.1183034$ or $b^2 = -0.118034$ the latter is invalid,

$b^2 = 2.1183034$

$b = \pm 1.46$

$a = \dfrac{1}{2\,(1.46)} = 0.343$ if $b = 1.46$

$a = -0.343$ if $b = -1.46$

therefore $\sqrt{i - 2} = \pm (0.343 + j\,1.46)$ and the square roots of $i - 2$ are

$0.343 + j1.46$ and $-0.343 - j1.46$.

9. $\quad I = 3 + j\,4 \quad |I| = \sqrt{3^2 + 4^2} = 5 \quad \arg I = \tan^{-1} 4/3 = 53.13°$

$\quad V = 5 + j\,5 \quad |V| = \sqrt{5^2 + 5^2} = 7.07, \quad \arg V = \tan^{-1} 5/5 = 45°$

the phase angle between V and I is $53.13° - 45°$
or 8.13^2, and $P = |\,I\,|\,|\,V\,|\,\cos \Phi = 5 \times 7.07 \times \cos 8.13°$ and
$P = 34.994 \approx 35W$.

10. (i) $\quad X_c = \dfrac{1}{2\pi f C} = \dfrac{1}{2\pi \; 50 \; 100 \times 10^{-6}} = 31.8 \; \Omega$

$X_L = 2\pi\,fL = 2\pi \; 50 \times 50 \times 10^{-3} = 15.71 \Omega$

$Z = R + j\,X_L - jX_c = 10 + j\,15.71 - j31.8$

$|Z| = \sqrt{10^2 + (15.71 - 31.8)^2} = 18.9\,\Omega$

$\arg Z = -\tan^{-1} \dfrac{31.8 - 15.71}{10} = -\tan^{-1}(3.18 - 1.571) = -58.14°$

(ii) $\quad Z = \dfrac{Z_1\,Z_2}{Z_1 + Z_2} = \dfrac{(5 - j\,8)\,(10 + j\,10)}{5 - j\,8 + 10 + j\,10} = \dfrac{-50 - j\,80 + j\,50 + 80}{15 + j\,2} = \dfrac{130 - j\,30}{15 + j\,2}$

$$|Z| = \frac{\sqrt{130^2 + (-30)^2}}{\sqrt{15^2 + 2^2}} = \frac{133.4}{15.1} = 8.815\,\Omega$$

arg Z = arg $(130 - j30)$ - arg $(15 + j2)$ = $- 12.99°$ - $7.595°$ = $- 20.6°$.

SOLUTION 4

1.

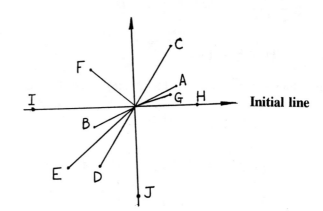

Fig. 84

2.

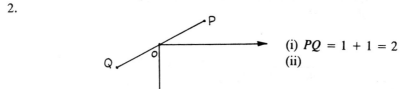

(i) $PQ = 1 + 1 = 2$

(ii)

Fig. 85

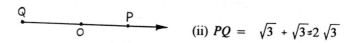

(ii) $PQ = \sqrt{3} + \sqrt{3} = 2\sqrt{3}$

Fig. 86

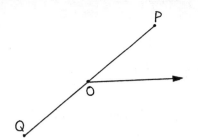

Fig. 87

(iii) $PQ = 4 + 4 = 8$

3.

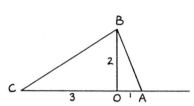

Fig. 88

Area $\Delta\ ABC \ = \dfrac{1}{2}\ (2)\ (1 + 3)$

$= 4$ square units.

4.　　(i)　　$\dfrac{x}{a} + \dfrac{y}{b} = 1$

$\sin \theta = y/r$ and $\cos \theta = x/r$
$y = r \sin \theta$ and $x = r \cos \theta$

$$\dfrac{r \cos \Theta}{a} + \dfrac{r \sin \Theta}{b} = 1$$

$$r = \dfrac{ab}{b \cos \Theta + a \sin \Theta}$$

(ii)　　$y = 3x - 5$
$x = r \cos \theta$ and $y = r \sin \theta$
$r \sin \theta = 3r \cos \theta \quad - 5$
$r (\sin \theta - 3\ \cos \theta) = - 5$

$$r = \dfrac{5}{3 \cos \Theta + \sin \Theta}$$

(iii)　$y = - 3x$

$r \sin \theta = - 3\ r \cos \theta$
$\sin \theta = - 3\ \ \cos \theta$
$\tan \theta = - 3$
$\theta = \tan (- 3)$

157

(iv) $y = x$

$r \sin \theta = r \cos \theta$
$\tan \theta = 1$
$\tan^{-1} 1 = \dfrac{\pi}{4}$

(v) $x = 5$ (vi) $y = 2$
$r \cos \theta = 5$ $r \sin \theta = 2$
$r = 5/\cos \theta$ $r = 2/\sin \theta$

(vii) $y = 0$ $r \sin \theta = 0$ or $\theta = 0°$

(viii) $y = x + 1$

$r \sin \theta = r \cos \theta + 1$
$r (\sin \theta - \cos \theta) = 1$

$$r = \dfrac{1}{\sin \Theta - \cos \Theta}$$

(ix) $x = -5$

$r \cos \theta = -5$
$r = -5/\cos \theta$

5.   (i) $x^2 + y^2 = 1$
$r^2 \cos^2 \theta + r^2 \sin^2 \theta = 1$
$r^2 (\cos^2 \Theta + \sin^2 \Theta) = 1$

(ii) $x^2 + y^2 = 2^2$
$r = 2$

(iii) $\dfrac{x^2}{3^2} + \dfrac{y^2}{4^2} = 1$

$$\dfrac{r^2 \cos^2 \Theta}{3^2} + \dfrac{r^2 \sin^2 \Theta}{4^2} = 1$$

$16 \, r_2 \cos_2 \theta + 9 \, r^2 \sin^2 \theta = 225$

(iv) $\dfrac{x^2}{4^2} - \dfrac{y^2}{5^2} = 1$

$\dfrac{r^2 \cos \Theta}{16} - \dfrac{r^2 \sin^2 \Theta}{25} = 1$

$25\, r^2 \cos^2 \Theta - 16\, r^2 \sin^2 \Theta = 400$

(v) $yx = 5$

$r \sin \Theta\; r \cos \Theta = 5$

$r^2 = \dfrac{4}{\sin \Theta \cos \Theta}$

(vi) $y^2 = 4x$

$r^2 \sin^2 \theta = 4r \cos \theta \qquad r = \dfrac{4 \cos \Theta}{\sin \Theta} = 4 \cos \Theta \operatorname{cosec}^2 \Theta$

(viii) $x^2 + y^2 - x - y - 1 = 0$

$r^2 \cos^2 \theta + r^2 \sin^2 \theta - r \cos \Theta - r \sin \theta = 0$

$r^2 (\cos^2 \Theta + \sin^2 \Theta) = r (\cos \Theta + \sin \Theta)$

$r = \cos \Theta + \sin \Theta$

(xi) $y = 1/x$

$r \sin \theta = 1/r \cos \theta$

$r^2 = \dfrac{1}{\sin \Theta \cos \Theta}$

6. (i) $r = 5 \Theta$

$r = \sqrt{x^2 + y^2}$

$$\Theta = \tan^{-1} y/x \qquad \sqrt{x^2 + y^2} = 5 \tan^{-1} \frac{y}{x}$$

(ii) $r = -3\,\Theta$

$$\boxed{\sqrt{x^2 + y^2} = -3 \tan^{-1} y/x}$$

(iii) $r = 2 \cos \Theta \qquad r^2 = 2x \qquad x^2 + y^2 = 2x$

$$\boxed{y/x = \tan \pi/4}$$

(iv) $\Theta = \pi/4$

$$\tan^{-1} y/x = \pi/4 \qquad y/x = \tan \pi/4 = 1$$

$$\boxed{y = x}$$

(v) $\Theta = \pi/2$

$$\tan^{-1} y/x = \pi/2 \quad \tan \pi/2 = y/x \quad y = x \tan \pi/2 \qquad \frac{y}{\tan \dfrac{\pi}{2}} = x$$

$$\boxed{x = 0}$$

(vi) $r = 1$

$$\sqrt{x^2 + y^2} = 1 \qquad x^2 + y^2 = 1$$

(vii) $r = 2^2 \qquad\qquad \sqrt{x^2 + y^2} = 4$

$$\boxed{x^2 + y^2 = 4^2.}$$

7. (i) $r = 5$

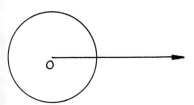

The radius of the circle is 5 and the centre is the pole.

(ii) $r = 3\theta$

If $\theta = 0$, $r = 0$
$\theta = \pi/3$ $r = \pi$
$\theta = \pi/2$, $r = 3\pi/2$
$\theta = \pi$, $r = 3\pi$

and $\theta = 2\pi$, $r = 6\pi$

(iii) $r = 3 \cos \theta$

Θ	0°	30°	60°	90°	120°	150°	180°
cos Θ	1	0.866	0.5	0	- 0.806	0.806	1
3 cos Θ	3	2.598	1.5	0	- 2.598	- 2.598	3

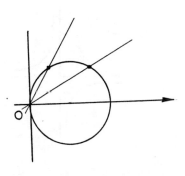

(iv) $\theta = \pi/3$

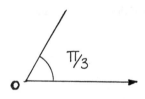

(v) $\theta = -\pi/2$

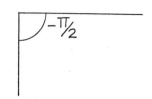

8. From the above examples, it can be seen that some functions in cartesian co-ordinate system are easy to be drawn and some functions in polar co-ordinate system are easy to be drawn.

EXAMPLES

(a) $y = x$ or $\theta = \pi/2$ is a straight line through the origin for $y = x$ and $\theta = \pi/2$ is a straight line drawn from the pole at 90°.

(b) $y = 1/x$ or $yx = 1$ is a simple cartesian curve, the rectangular hyperbola

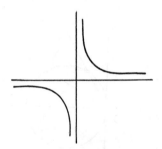

but the corresponding polar curve is $r^2 = \dfrac{1}{\sin\Theta\cos\Theta}$

which is rather difficult to recognise, a table needs to be constructed for various angles and the corresponding values of r to be calculated.

(c) $r = 3\theta$ is an archimediam spiral which is easy to be

drawn, but the corresponding cartesian form is

$$\sqrt{x^2 + y^2} = 3\tan^{-1}\frac{y}{x}$$ which would be rather very

difficult to interpret.

SOLUTIONS 5

1.   (i) $\begin{pmatrix} 1 & 0 \\ 0 & 1 \end{pmatrix}$ unit matrix 2 x 2

       (ii) $\begin{pmatrix} 0 & 0 \\ 0 & 0 \end{pmatrix}$ zero matrix 2 x 2

       (iii) $\begin{pmatrix} 3 & 0 \\ 0 & -2 \end{pmatrix}$ diagional matrix 2 x 2

2.   (i) $\begin{pmatrix} a \\ b \\ c \end{pmatrix}$ 3 x 1 column matrix

       (ii) $\begin{pmatrix} 1 & 2 & 3 \\ 4 & 5 & 6 \\ 7 & 8 & 9 \end{pmatrix}$ 3 x 3 square matrix

       (iii) $\begin{pmatrix} a & b & c \end{pmatrix}$ 1 x 3 matrix

(iv)
$$\begin{pmatrix} a & d \\ b & e \\ c & f \end{pmatrix}$$
3 x 2 rectangular matrix

$$\begin{pmatrix} a & b & c \\ d & e & f \end{pmatrix}$$
2 x 3 rectangular matrix

(v)
$$\begin{pmatrix} 1 & 0 & 0 \\ 0 & 1 & 0 \\ 0 & 0 & 1 \end{pmatrix}$$
3 x 3 unit matrix

(vi)
$$\begin{pmatrix} a & 0 & 0 \\ 0 & b & 0 \\ 0 & 0 & c \end{pmatrix}$$
3 x 3 diagonal matrix

(viii)
$$\begin{pmatrix} 0 & 0 & 0 \\ 0 & 0 & 0 \\ 0 & 0 & 0 \end{pmatrix}$$
3 x 3 Null matrix.

3. $A = \begin{pmatrix} -1 & 2 \\ -3 & 3 \end{pmatrix}$ $B = \begin{pmatrix} 1 & -2 \\ 3 & 5 \end{pmatrix}$ $C = \begin{pmatrix} 0 & 1 \\ 1 & 0 \end{pmatrix}$

(i) $A + B + C = \begin{pmatrix} -1 & 2 \\ -3 & 3 \end{pmatrix} + \begin{pmatrix} 1 & -2 \\ 3 & 5 \end{pmatrix} + \begin{pmatrix} 0 & 1 \\ 1 & 0 \end{pmatrix}$

$= \begin{pmatrix} -1+1+0 & 2-2+1 \\ -3+3+1 & 3+5+0 \end{pmatrix} = \begin{pmatrix} 0 & 1 \\ 1 & 8 \end{pmatrix}$

(ii) $2A - 3C + 2B = 2\begin{pmatrix} -1 & 2 \\ -3 & 3 \end{pmatrix} - 3\begin{pmatrix} 0 & 1 \\ 1 & 0 \end{pmatrix} + 2\begin{pmatrix} 1 & -2 \\ 3 & 5 \end{pmatrix}$

$$= \begin{pmatrix} -2 & 4 \\ -6 & 6 \end{pmatrix} - \begin{pmatrix} 0 & 3 \\ 3 & 0 \end{pmatrix} + \begin{pmatrix} 2 & -4 \\ 6 & 10 \end{pmatrix}$$

$$= \begin{pmatrix} -2-0+2 & 4-3-4 \\ -6-3+6 & 6-0+10 \end{pmatrix} = \begin{pmatrix} 0 & -3 \\ -3 & 15 \end{pmatrix}$$

(iii) $\quad 5B + 4A = 5 \begin{pmatrix} 1 & -2 \\ 3 & 5 \end{pmatrix} + 4 \begin{pmatrix} -1 & 2 \\ -3 & 3 \end{pmatrix} = \begin{pmatrix} 5 & -10 \\ 15 & 25 \end{pmatrix} + \begin{pmatrix} -4 & 8 \\ -12 & 12 \end{pmatrix}$

$$= \begin{pmatrix} 5-4 & -10+8 \\ 15+12 & 25+12 \end{pmatrix} = \begin{pmatrix} 1 & -2 \\ 17 & 37 \end{pmatrix}$$

4. $\quad A = \begin{pmatrix} 6 & 7 \\ 8 & 9 \end{pmatrix} \quad B = \begin{pmatrix} 10 & 11 \\ 12 & 13 \end{pmatrix} \quad C = \begin{pmatrix} 0 & 1 \\ -1 & 0 \end{pmatrix}$

(i) $\quad AB = \begin{pmatrix} 6 & 7 \\ 8 & 9 \end{pmatrix} \begin{pmatrix} 10 & 11 \\ \downarrow 12 & 13 \end{pmatrix} = \begin{pmatrix} 60+84 & 66+91 \\ 80+108 & 88+117 \end{pmatrix} = \begin{pmatrix} 144 & 157 \\ 188 & 205 \end{pmatrix}$

$ABC = \begin{pmatrix} 144 & 157 \\ 188 & 205 \end{pmatrix} \begin{pmatrix} 0 & 1 \\ -1 & 0 \end{pmatrix} = \begin{pmatrix} -157 & 144 \\ -205 & 188 \end{pmatrix}$

(ii) $\quad A^2 = A\,A = \begin{pmatrix} 6 & 7 \\ 8 & 9 \end{pmatrix} \begin{pmatrix} 6 & 7 \\ 8 & 9 \end{pmatrix} = \begin{pmatrix} 36+56 & 42+63 \\ 48+72 & 56+81 \end{pmatrix}$

$$= \begin{pmatrix} 92 & 105 \\ 120 & 137 \end{pmatrix}$$

(iii) $\quad BC = \begin{pmatrix} 10 & 11 \\ 12 & 13 \end{pmatrix} \begin{pmatrix} 0 & 1 \\ -1 & 0 \end{pmatrix} = \begin{pmatrix} 10 \times 0 + 11(-1) & 10 + 11(0) \\ 12 \times 1 + 13(-1) & 12 \times 1 + 13(0) \end{pmatrix}$

$$= \begin{pmatrix} -11 & 10 \\ -13 & 12 \end{pmatrix}$$

(iv)
$$= \begin{pmatrix} 6 & 7 \\ 8 & 9 \end{pmatrix} \begin{pmatrix} 0 & 1 \\ -1 & 0 \end{pmatrix} = \begin{pmatrix} 6 \times 0 + 7(-1) & 6 \times 1 + 7(0) \\ 8(0) + 9(-1) & 8 \times 1 + 9(0) \end{pmatrix}$$

$$= \begin{pmatrix} -7 & 6 \\ -9 & 8 \end{pmatrix}$$

(v) $CB = \begin{pmatrix} 0 & 1 \\ -1 & 0 \end{pmatrix} \begin{pmatrix} 10 & 11 \\ 12 & 13 \end{pmatrix} = \begin{pmatrix} 12 & 13 \\ -10 & -11 \end{pmatrix}$

5. $AB = \begin{pmatrix} 144 & 157 \\ 188 & 205 \end{pmatrix}$ $BA = \begin{pmatrix} 10 & 11 \\ 12 & 13 \end{pmatrix} \begin{pmatrix} 6 & 7 \\ 8 & 9 \end{pmatrix}$

$$= \begin{pmatrix} 60 + 88 & 70 + 99 \\ 72 + 104 & 84 + 117 \end{pmatrix} = \begin{pmatrix} 148 & 169 \\ 176 & 201 \end{pmatrix}$$

therefore **AB ≠ BA**.

$BC = \begin{pmatrix} -11 & 10 \\ -13 & 12 \end{pmatrix}$ $CB = \begin{pmatrix} 0 & 1 \\ -1 & 0 \end{pmatrix} \begin{pmatrix} 10 & 11 \\ 12 & 13 \end{pmatrix} = \begin{pmatrix} 12 & 13 \\ -10 & -11 \end{pmatrix}$

therefore **BC ≠ CB**.

6. **A + B = B + A** using the examples of question 5

$$A + B = \begin{pmatrix} 6 & 7 \\ 8 & 9 \end{pmatrix} + \begin{pmatrix} 10 & 11 \\ 12 & 13 \end{pmatrix} = \begin{pmatrix} 16 & 18 \\ 20 & 22 \end{pmatrix}$$

$$B + A = \begin{pmatrix} 10 & 11 \\ 12 & 13 \end{pmatrix} + \begin{pmatrix} 6 & 7 \\ 8 & 9 \end{pmatrix} = \begin{pmatrix} 16 & 18 \\ 20 & 22 \end{pmatrix}$$

therefore $A + B = B + A$ the matrices are associative.

In question five, we have seen that $AB \neq BA$ and $\neq CB$ therefore matrices are not commutative.

7. A unit matrix is a diagonal matrix whose elements are one.

$$I = \begin{pmatrix} 1 & 0 \\ 0 & 1 \end{pmatrix} \quad A = \begin{pmatrix} 1 & -2 \\ 3 & -4 \end{pmatrix}$$

$$IA = \begin{pmatrix} 1 & 0 \\ 0 & 1 \end{pmatrix} \begin{pmatrix} 1 & -2 \\ 3 & -4 \end{pmatrix} = \begin{pmatrix} 1 & -2 \\ 3 & -4 \end{pmatrix}.$$

Matrix A is unaltered when it is premultiplied by a unit matrix

$$AI = \begin{pmatrix} 1 & -2 \\ 3 & -4 \end{pmatrix} \begin{pmatrix} 1 & 0 \\ 0 & 1 \end{pmatrix} = \begin{pmatrix} 1 & -2 \\ 3 & -4 \end{pmatrix}$$

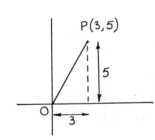

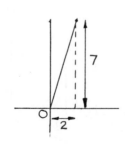

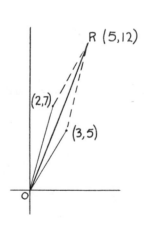

Matrix A is unaltered when it is post multiplied by a unit matrix

$$P + OQ = \begin{pmatrix} 3 \\ 5 \end{pmatrix} + \begin{pmatrix} 2 \\ 7 \end{pmatrix} = \begin{pmatrix} 3 + 2 \\ 5 + 7 \end{pmatrix} = \begin{pmatrix} 5 \\ 12 \end{pmatrix}$$

$$OR = \begin{pmatrix} 5 \\ 12 \end{pmatrix}$$

9. $\quad A = \begin{pmatrix} 1 & b \\ a & 2 \end{pmatrix} \quad B = \begin{pmatrix} -1 & 2 \\ 3 & 4 \end{pmatrix}$

$$AB = \begin{pmatrix} 1 & b \\ a & 2 \end{pmatrix} \begin{pmatrix} -1 & 2 \\ 3 & 4 \end{pmatrix} = \begin{pmatrix} -1 + 3b & 2 + 4b \\ -a + b & 2a + 8 \end{pmatrix}$$

$$C = \begin{pmatrix} 5 & 10 \\ -1 & 22 \end{pmatrix}$$

AB = C

therefore the corresponding elements are equal

$$-1 + 3b = 5 \Rightarrow 3b = 6 \Rightarrow b = 2$$
$$2 + 4b = 10 \Rightarrow 4b = 8 \Rightarrow b = 2$$
$$-a + b = -5 \Rightarrow -a = -7 \Rightarrow a = 7$$
$$2a + 8 = 22 \Rightarrow 2a = 14 \Rightarrow a = 7$$

$a = 7$ and $b = 2$

10. $\quad$ (i)
$$\begin{vmatrix} a & b \\ a^2 & b^2 \end{vmatrix} = a \begin{vmatrix} 1 & b \\ a & b^2 \end{vmatrix} = ab \begin{vmatrix} 1 & 1 \\ a & b \end{vmatrix} = ab(b - a)$$

factorising

(ii)
$$\begin{vmatrix} 1 & 3 \\ 2 & 4 \end{vmatrix} = 1 \times 4 - 2 \times 3 = 4 - 6 = -2$$

168

(ii) $\begin{vmatrix} 1 & 3 \\ 2 & 4 \end{vmatrix} = 1 \times 4 - 2 \times 3 = 4 - 6 = -2$

(iii) $\begin{vmatrix} a & 3 \\ 4 & a \end{vmatrix} = a^2 - 12$

11. (i) $\begin{vmatrix} a & 2 \\ a^2 & 4 \end{vmatrix} = a \begin{vmatrix} 1 & 2 \\ a & 4 \end{vmatrix} = 2a \begin{vmatrix} 1 & 1 \\ a & 2 \end{vmatrix}$

If the two columns are equal the determinant is zero, therefore $a = 2$.

(ii) $\begin{vmatrix} 3 & 2 \\ 9 & a^2 \end{vmatrix} = \begin{vmatrix} 1 & a \\ 3 & a^2 \end{vmatrix} = \begin{vmatrix} 1 & 1 \\ 3 & a \end{vmatrix}$

therefore $a = 3$ and the columns are the same and hence the Δ is zero.

(iii) $\begin{vmatrix} 1 & a \\ a & 1 \end{vmatrix}$

If $a = 1$ then the $\Delta = 0$.

12. (i) $\begin{vmatrix} 2x & 1 \\ 8x^2 & 2 \end{vmatrix} = 2x \begin{vmatrix} 1 & 1 \\ 4x & 2 \end{vmatrix} = 2x\,(2 - 4x)$

(ii) $= 2 \times 2 \begin{vmatrix} 1 & 1 \\ 2x & 1 \end{vmatrix} = 4x(1 - 2x)$

$\begin{vmatrix} 2y & y \\ 4y^2 & x^2 \end{vmatrix} = 2y \begin{vmatrix} 1 & x \\ 2y & x^2 \end{vmatrix} = 2xy \begin{vmatrix} 1 & 1 \\ 2y & x \end{vmatrix}$

$= 2xy(x - 2y)$

SOLUTION 6

1.   (i) $2x - y = 5 \ldots(1)$
$x + y = -7 \ldots(2)$

Adding equations (1) and (2)

$3x = -2$ or $x = -2/3$

substituting $x = -2/3$ in (2)

$-\dfrac{2}{3} + y = 7$ or $y = -7 + \dfrac{2}{3} = -6\dfrac{1}{3} = -19/3$

therefore $x = -2/3$ and $y = -19/3$.

(ii) $-3x + 2y = 2 \ldots(1)$
$x - 3y = 5 \ldots(2)$

multiply (2) by 3, we have $3x - 9y = 15 \ldots(3)$
equations (1) and (3) are

$-3x + 2y = 2 \ldots(3)$
$3x - 9y = 15 \ldots(4)$

adding equations (3) and (4)

$-7y = 17$ or $y = -17/7$

substituting $y = -17/7$ in equation (2)

$$x - 3\left(-\frac{17}{7}\right) = \quad \text{or} \quad x = 5 - \frac{51}{7} = \frac{35 - 51}{7}$$

$x = -16/7$

therefore $x = -16/7$ and $y = -17/7$

2.　　　(i)　　　$2x - y = 5$
　　　　　　　$x + y = -7$

using Crammer's rule

$$\frac{x}{\Delta_1} = -\frac{y}{\Delta_2} = \frac{1}{\Delta}$$

where $\Delta_1 = \begin{vmatrix} -1 & -5 \\ 1 & 7 \end{vmatrix} = -7 + 5 = -2$

$\Delta_2 = \begin{vmatrix} 2 & -5 \\ 1 & 7 \end{vmatrix} = 14 + 5 = 19$

$\Delta = \begin{vmatrix} 2 & -1 \\ 1 & 1 \end{vmatrix} = 2 + 1 = 3$

$\dfrac{x}{\Delta_1} = \dfrac{1}{\Delta}$　　or　　$x = \dfrac{\Delta_1}{\Delta} = -\dfrac{2}{3}$

$$\frac{y}{\Delta_2} = \frac{1}{\Delta} \qquad \text{or} \quad y = -\frac{\Delta_2}{\Delta} = -\frac{19}{3}$$

therefore $x = -\dfrac{2}{3}$ and $y = -\dfrac{19}{3}$

(ii) $\quad -3x + 2y = 2$
$\qquad\quad x - 3y = 5$

Using Crammer's rule

$$\frac{x}{\Delta_1} = -\frac{y}{\Delta_2} = \frac{1}{\Delta}$$

Where $\quad \Delta_1 = \begin{vmatrix} 2 & -2 \\ -3 & -5 \end{vmatrix}$, $\Delta_2 = \begin{vmatrix} -3 & -2 \\ 1 & -5 \end{vmatrix}$, $\Delta = \begin{vmatrix} -3 & 2 \\ 1 & -3 \end{vmatrix}$

$\Delta_1 = -10 - 6 = -16, \Delta_2 = 15 + 2 = 17, \Delta = 9 - 2 = 7$

$$x = \frac{\Delta_1}{\Delta} = -\frac{16}{7} \quad \text{and} \quad y = -\frac{\Delta_2}{\Delta} = -\frac{17}{7}$$

and therefore $x = -16/7$ and $y = -17/7$.

3. (i) $\quad A = \begin{pmatrix} 1 & 2 \\ 3 & 4 \end{pmatrix}$

the minors are $\begin{pmatrix} 4 & 3 \\ 2 & 1 \end{pmatrix}$

and the corresponding cofactors are $\begin{pmatrix} 4 & -3 \\ -2 & 1 \end{pmatrix}$

(ii)   (i) $M = \begin{pmatrix} -1 & -2 \\ -3 & 4 \end{pmatrix}$

the minors are $\begin{pmatrix} 4 & -3 \\ -2 & -1 \end{pmatrix}$ and hence the cofactors

are $\begin{pmatrix} 4 & 3 \\ 2 & -1 \end{pmatrix}$

4.   (i) $A = \begin{pmatrix} 1 & 2 \\ 3 & 4 \end{pmatrix}$

$A^* = \begin{pmatrix} 4 & -3 \\ -2 & 1 \end{pmatrix}$

A^* the cofactors of A^{*T} adjoint matrix $= \begin{pmatrix} 4 & -2 \\ -3 & 1 \end{pmatrix}$

(ii) $M = \begin{pmatrix} -1 & -2 \\ -3 & 4 \end{pmatrix}$

$M^* = \begin{pmatrix} 4 & 3 \\ 2 & -1 \end{pmatrix}$ $M^{*T} =$ the transpose of the cofactors $=$ adjoint matrix.

$= \begin{pmatrix} 4 & 2 \\ 3 & -1 \end{pmatrix}$

5.   (i) $A = \begin{pmatrix} 2 & -1 \\ 2 & 1 \end{pmatrix}$

$$A^{*T} = \begin{pmatrix} 1 & 1 \\ -2 & 2 \end{pmatrix}$$

$$|A| = \begin{vmatrix} 2 & -1 \\ 2 & 1 \end{vmatrix} = 2 + 2 = 4$$

$$A^{-1} = \frac{A^{*T}}{|A|} = \frac{1}{4} \begin{pmatrix} 1 & 1 \\ -2 & 2 \end{pmatrix} = \begin{pmatrix} \frac{1}{4} & \frac{1}{4} \\ -\frac{1}{2} & \frac{1}{2} \end{pmatrix}$$

(ii) $$B = \begin{pmatrix} -3 & 2 \\ 1 & -3 \end{pmatrix}$$

$$B^* = \begin{pmatrix} -3 & -1 \\ -2 & -3 \end{pmatrix} \qquad B^{*T} \begin{pmatrix} -3 & -2 \\ -1 & -3 \end{pmatrix}$$

$$|B| \begin{vmatrix} -3 & 2 \\ 1 & -3 \end{vmatrix} = 9 - 2 = 7$$

$$B^{-1} = \frac{B^{*T}}{|B|} = \frac{1}{7} \begin{pmatrix} -3 & -2 \\ -1 & -3 \end{pmatrix} = \begin{pmatrix} -\frac{3}{7} & -\frac{2}{7} \\ -\frac{1}{7} & -\frac{3}{7} \end{pmatrix}$$

6.   (ii) $2x - y = 5$
$x + y = -7$

In matrix form

$$\begin{pmatrix} 2 & -1 \\ 1 & 1 \end{pmatrix} \begin{pmatrix} x \\ y \end{pmatrix} = \begin{pmatrix} 5 \\ -7 \end{pmatrix}$$

If $A = \begin{pmatrix} 2 & -1 \\ 1 & 1 \end{pmatrix}$

$A^* = \begin{pmatrix} 1 & -1 \\ 1 & 2 \end{pmatrix}$

$A^{*T} = \begin{pmatrix} 1 & 1 \\ -1 & 2 \end{pmatrix}$

$|A| = \begin{vmatrix} 2 & -1 \\ 1 & 1 \end{vmatrix} = 2 + 1 = 3$

$A^{-1} = \dfrac{A^{*T}}{|A|} = \begin{pmatrix} \dfrac{1}{3} & \dfrac{1}{3} \\ -\dfrac{1}{3} & \dfrac{2}{3} \end{pmatrix}$

$A^{-1}A = \begin{pmatrix} \dfrac{1}{3} & \dfrac{1}{3} \\ -\dfrac{1}{3} & \dfrac{2}{3} \end{pmatrix} \begin{pmatrix} 2 & -1 \\ 1 & 1 \end{pmatrix} = \begin{pmatrix} \dfrac{2}{3} + \dfrac{1}{3} & -\dfrac{1}{3} + \dfrac{1}{3} \\ -\dfrac{2}{3} + \dfrac{2}{3} & \dfrac{1}{3} + \dfrac{2}{3} \end{pmatrix}$

$= \begin{pmatrix} 1 & 0 \\ 0 & 1 \end{pmatrix} = I$

$$\begin{pmatrix} \dfrac{1}{3} & \dfrac{1}{3} \\ -\dfrac{1}{3} & \dfrac{2}{3} \end{pmatrix} \begin{pmatrix} 2 & -1 \\ 1 & 1 \end{pmatrix} \begin{pmatrix} x \\ y \end{pmatrix} = \begin{pmatrix} \dfrac{1}{3} & \dfrac{1}{3} \\ -\dfrac{1}{3} & \dfrac{2}{3} \end{pmatrix} \begin{pmatrix} 5 \\ -7 \end{pmatrix}$$

$$\begin{pmatrix} x \\ y \end{pmatrix} = \begin{pmatrix} \dfrac{5}{3} & -\dfrac{7}{3} \\ -\dfrac{5}{3} & -\dfrac{14}{3} \end{pmatrix} = \begin{pmatrix} -\dfrac{2}{3} \\ -\dfrac{19}{3} \end{pmatrix}$$

$x = 2/3$ and $y = -19/3$.

(ii) $-3x + 2y = 2$

$x - 3y = 5$

In matrix form

$$\begin{pmatrix} -3 & 2 \\ 1 & -3 \end{pmatrix} \begin{pmatrix} x \\ y \end{pmatrix} = \begin{pmatrix} 2 \\ 5 \end{pmatrix}$$

Let $B = \begin{pmatrix} -3 & 2 \\ 1 & -3 \end{pmatrix}$, $B^{-1} = \begin{pmatrix} -\dfrac{3}{7} & -\dfrac{2}{7} \\ -\dfrac{1}{7} & -\dfrac{3}{7} \end{pmatrix}$

See solution 5 (ii)

$$B^{-1}B \quad \begin{pmatrix} -\dfrac{2}{7} & -\dfrac{2}{7} \\ -\dfrac{1}{7} & -\dfrac{3}{7} \end{pmatrix} \begin{pmatrix} -3 & 2 \\ 1 & -3 \end{pmatrix} = \begin{pmatrix} \dfrac{9}{7} + \dfrac{2}{7} & -\dfrac{6}{7} + \dfrac{6}{7} \\ \dfrac{3}{7} - \dfrac{3}{7} & -\dfrac{2}{7} + \dfrac{9}{7} \end{pmatrix}$$

$$\begin{pmatrix} -\dfrac{3}{7} & -\dfrac{2}{7} \\ -\dfrac{1}{7} & -\dfrac{3}{7} \end{pmatrix} \begin{pmatrix} -3 & 2 \\ 1 & -3 \end{pmatrix} \begin{pmatrix} x \\ y \end{pmatrix} = \begin{pmatrix} -\dfrac{3}{7} & -\dfrac{2}{7} \\ -\dfrac{1}{7} & -\dfrac{3}{7} \end{pmatrix} \begin{pmatrix} 2 \\ 5 \end{pmatrix}$$

$$\begin{pmatrix} x \\ y \end{pmatrix} = \begin{pmatrix} -\dfrac{6}{7} & -\dfrac{10}{7} \\ -\dfrac{2}{7} & -\dfrac{15}{7} \end{pmatrix} = \begin{pmatrix} -\dfrac{16}{7} \\ -\dfrac{17}{7} \end{pmatrix}$$

and therefore $x = -16/7$ and $y = -17/7$.

7.   Using Kirchhoff's Law

$$10 = 2 I_1 + 5 I_1 + 5I_2$$

$$\boxed{10 = 7 I_1 + 5 I_2}$$

$$5 = 1.5 I_2 + 5 I_1 + 5 I_2$$

$$\boxed{5 = 5I_1 + 6.5 I_2}$$

(i) $7I_1 + 5 I_2 = 10$

$5I_1 + 6.5 I_2 = 5$

by Crammer's rule.

$$\frac{I_1}{\Delta_1} = -\frac{I_2}{\Delta_2} = \frac{1}{\Delta}$$

$$\Delta_1 = \begin{vmatrix} 5 & -10 \\ 6.5 & -5 \end{vmatrix} = 25 + 65 = 40$$

$$\Delta_2 = \begin{vmatrix} 7 & -10 \\ 5 & -5 \end{vmatrix} = -35 + 50 = 15$$

$$\Delta = \begin{vmatrix} 7 & 5 \\ 5 & 6.5 \end{vmatrix} = 45 - 25 = 20$$

$$I_1 = \frac{\Delta_1}{\Delta} = \frac{40}{20} = 2A$$

$$I_2 = -\frac{\Delta_2}{\Delta} = -\frac{15}{20} = -0.75A$$

(ii)   In matrix form

$$\begin{pmatrix} 7 & 5 \\ 5 & 6.5 \end{pmatrix} \begin{pmatrix} I_1 \\ I_2 \end{pmatrix} = \begin{pmatrix} 10 \\ 5 \end{pmatrix}$$

$$A = \begin{pmatrix} 7 & 5 \\ 5 & 6.5 \end{pmatrix}$$

$$A^* = \begin{pmatrix} 6.5 & -5 \\ -5 & 7 \end{pmatrix} \qquad A^{*T} = \begin{pmatrix} 6.5 & -5 \\ -5 & 7 \end{pmatrix}$$

$$A^{-1} = \frac{A^{*T}}{|A|} = \frac{\begin{pmatrix} 6.5 & -5 \\ -5 & 7 \end{pmatrix}}{\begin{pmatrix} 7 & 5 \\ 5 & 6.5 \end{pmatrix}} = \frac{\begin{pmatrix} 6.5 & -5 \\ -5 & 7 \end{pmatrix}}{20} = \begin{pmatrix} \dfrac{6.5}{20} & \dfrac{5}{20} \\ -\dfrac{5}{20} & \dfrac{7}{20} \end{pmatrix}$$

$$A^{-1} A = \begin{pmatrix} 0.325 & -0.25 \\ -0.25 & 0.35 \end{pmatrix} \begin{pmatrix} 7 & 5 \\ 5 & 6.5 \end{pmatrix} = \begin{pmatrix} 1 & 0 \\ 0 & 1 \end{pmatrix}$$

$$I \begin{pmatrix} I_1 \\ I_2 \end{pmatrix} \begin{pmatrix} 0.325 & -0.25 \\ -0.25 & 0.35 \end{pmatrix} \begin{pmatrix} 10 \\ 5 \end{pmatrix} = \begin{pmatrix} 2 \\ -0.75 \end{pmatrix}$$

$$\begin{pmatrix} I_1 \\ I_2 \end{pmatrix} = \begin{pmatrix} 2 \\ -0.75 \end{pmatrix}$$

$I_1 = 2$ and $I_2 = -0.75$.

8. From the network, we have

$$V_{be} = i_b\, 1000 + 10^4\, V_{ce} \ \ldots(1)$$

$$i_c = 100\, i_b + 10^3\, V_{ce} \ \ldots(2)$$

$$V_{be} = i_b\, 1000 + 10^4\, V_{ce} \ \ldots(3)$$

$$\frac{V_{ce}}{-1000} = 100\, i_b + 10^{-3}\, V_{ce} \ \ldots(4)$$

eliminate i_b by multiplying (4) by 10

$$V_{be} = 1000\, i_b + 10^{-4}\, V_{ce}$$

$$-\frac{V_{ce}}{100} = 1000\, i_b + 10^{-2}\, V_{ce}$$

$$V_{be} + \frac{V_{ce}}{100} = \left(10^{-4} - 10^{-2}\right) V_{ce}$$

$$V_{be} = V_{ce}\, (10^{-4} - 10^{-2} - 10^{-2})$$

$$= V_{ce}\, (10^{-4} - 2 \times 10^{-2})$$

$$\frac{V_{ce}}{V_{be}} = \frac{1}{-(0.02 - 0.0001)} = -50.3$$

$$\frac{V_{ce}}{V_{be}} = 50.3.$$

(ii) $\quad \dfrac{i_c}{i_b}$ can be found as follows

$$i_c = 100\, i_b + 10^{-3}\, (-1000\, i_c)$$

$$i_c\, (1 + 1) = 100\, i_b$$

$$\frac{i_c}{i_b} = \frac{100}{2} = 50.$$

SOLUTION 7

1. (i) $\quad (1 - 5x)^{-3} = 1 + (-3)\,(-5x) + (-3)\,(-4)\,(-5x)^2\, \dfrac{1}{2} = 1 + 15x + 150$

(ii) $\quad 1 + 3x)^{3/4} = 1 + \dfrac{3}{4}\,(3x) + \left(\dfrac{3}{4}\right)\left(-\dfrac{1}{4}\right)(3x)^2\, \dfrac{1}{2} = 1 + \dfrac{9}{4}x - \dfrac{27}{32}\,x^2.$

(iii) $\quad (1 - 4x)^{-1/3} = 1 + \left(-\dfrac{1}{3}\right)(-4x) + \left(-\dfrac{1}{3}\right)\left(-\dfrac{4}{3}\right)(-4x)^2\, \dfrac{1}{2} = 1 + \dfrac{4}{3}x + \dfrac{32}{9}$

(iv) $\quad (1 - x)^{1/2} = 1 + \dfrac{1}{2}\,(-x) + \left(\dfrac{1}{2}\right)\left(-\dfrac{1}{2}\right)(-x)^2\, \dfrac{1}{2} = 1 - \dfrac{1}{2}x - \dfrac{1}{8}x^2.$

(v) $\quad (1 + x)^{-1/2} = 1 + \left(-\dfrac{1}{2}\right)x + \left(-\dfrac{1}{2}\right)\left(-\dfrac{3}{2}\right)x^2\, \dfrac{1}{2} = 1 - \dfrac{1}{2}x + \dfrac{3}{8}\,x^2.$

2. (i) $\quad (1 + px)^n = 1 + n\, px + n\,(n - 1)\, p^2\, x^2\, \dfrac{1}{2}.$

2.

(i)
$$(1 + px)^n = 1 + n\,px + n\,(n - 1)\,p^2\,x^2\,\frac{1}{2}.$$

(ii)
$$(1 - px)^{-n} = 1 + (-n)\,(-px) + (-n)\,(-n - 1)\,(-px)^2\,\frac{1}{2}.$$

$$= 1 + n\,px + \frac{1}{2}\,n\,(n + 1)\,p^2\,x^2.$$

(iii)
$$(1 + 3ax)^{-n} = 1 + (-n)\,(3ax) + (-n)\,(-n - 1)\,(3ax)^2\,\frac{1}{2}.$$

$$= 1 - 3\,anx + \frac{9}{2}\,n\,(n + 1)\,a^2\,x^2.$$

(iv)
$$(1 - 2bx)^n = 1 + n\,(-2bx) + n\,(n - 1)\,(-2bx)^2\,\frac{1}{2}.$$

$$= 1 - 2n\,bx + 2n\,(n - 1)\,b^2\,x^2.$$

(v)
$$(1 - bx)^n = 1 + n\,(-bx) + n\,(n - 1)\,(-bx)^2\,\frac{1}{2}.$$

3.

(i)
$$\frac{\sqrt{1 - y}}{\sqrt{1 + y}} = (1 - y)^{1/2}\,(1 + y)^{-1/2} = \left[1 + \frac{1}{2}(-y) + \frac{1}{2}\left(-\frac{1}{2}\right)(-y)^2\,\frac{1}{2}\right]$$

$$\times \left[1 - \frac{1}{2}\,y + \left(-\frac{1}{2}\right)\left(-\frac{3}{2}\right)(y^2)\,\frac{1}{2}\right]$$

$$= \left(1 - \frac{1}{2}y - \frac{1}{8}y^2\right)\left(1 - \frac{1}{2}y + \frac{3}{8}y^2\right)$$

$$= 1 - \frac{1}{2}y + \frac{3}{8}\,y^2 - \frac{1}{2}y + \frac{1}{4}\,y^2 - \frac{1}{8}\,y^2$$

$$= 1 - y + \frac{1}{2}\,y^2.$$

(ii)
$$\frac{1}{\sqrt{1 - y^2}} = (1 - y^2)^{-1/2} = 1 + \left(-\frac{1}{2}\right)(-y^2) + \left(-\frac{1}{2}\right)\left(-\frac{3}{2}\right)(-y^2)^2\,\frac{1}{2}$$

$$= 1 - \frac{1}{2}\,y^2 + \frac{3}{8}\,y^4.$$

181

(iii)
$$\sqrt{9 + ay} = \sqrt{9\left(1 + \frac{ay}{9}\right)} = 3\left(1 + \frac{ay}{9}\right)^{1/2}$$

$$= 3\left(1 + \frac{1}{2}\frac{ay}{9} + \frac{1}{2}\left(-\frac{1}{}\right)\qquad\right)$$

$$= 3 + \frac{1}{6}ay - \frac{1}{216}a^2 y^2.$$

(iv)
$$\frac{1}{\sqrt{16 - by}} = (16 - by)^{-1/2} = 16^{-1/2}\left(1 - \frac{by}{16}\right)^{-1/2}$$

$$= \frac{1}{4}\left(1 + \left(-\frac{1}{2}\right)\left(-\frac{by}{16}\right) + \left(-\frac{1}{2}\right)\left(-\frac{3}{2}\right)\left(\frac{by}{16}\right)^2 \frac{1}{2}\right)$$

$$= \frac{1}{4} + \frac{by}{128} + \frac{3 b^2}{8192}y^2.$$

4.
$$(25 + x)^{1/2} = 5(1 + x/25)^{1/2} = 5\left(1 + \frac{1}{2}\frac{x}{25} + \frac{1}{2}\left(-\frac{1}{2}\right)\left(\frac{x}{25}\right)^2 \frac{1}{2}\right)$$

$$= 5 + \frac{x}{10} - \frac{x^2}{1000}.$$

5. (i)
$$(1 + 2x)^{1/3} = 1 + \frac{1}{3}(2x) + \frac{1}{3}\left(-\frac{2}{3}\right)(2x)^2 \frac{1}{2} + \frac{1}{3}\left(-\frac{2}{3}\right)\left(-\frac{5}{3}\right)(2x)^3 \frac{1}{3!}$$

$$= 1 + \frac{2}{3}x - \frac{4}{9}x^2 + \frac{40}{81}x^3.$$

(ii)
$$(1 - 3x)^{1/5} = 1 + \left(-\frac{1}{5}\right)(-3x) + \left(-\frac{1}{5}\right)\left(-\frac{6}{5}\right)(-3x)^2 \frac{1}{2}$$

$$+ \left(-\frac{1}{5}\right)(-6/5)\left(-\frac{11}{5}\right)(-3x)^3) \frac{1}{3!}$$

$$\frac{a^2 y^2}{2} \frac{1}{81} \frac{1}{2}$$

$$(1 + 2x)^{1/3} \, x + 25 \, (1 - 3x)^{1/5} = a + bx + cx^2 + dx^3 + \ldots$$

$$1 + \frac{2}{3} x - \frac{4}{9} x^2 + \frac{40}{81} x^3 + 25 + 15 x + 27 x^2 - 15 x^3$$

$$= a + bx + cx^2 + dx^3$$

equating coefficients

$$a = 26, \quad b = \frac{2}{3} + 15 = \frac{47}{3}, \quad c = -\frac{4}{9} + 27 = \frac{239}{9}$$

and $\quad d = \dfrac{40}{81} + \dfrac{297}{5} = \dfrac{200 + 24057}{405} = \dfrac{24257}{405}$

$$\boxed{a = 26} \qquad \boxed{b = \frac{47}{3}} \qquad \boxed{c = \frac{239}{9}} \qquad \boxed{d = \frac{24{,}257}{405}}$$

6. (i) $(1 + 2x)^{1/2} \, (1 - 3x)^{-1/2} = \left[1 + \left(\dfrac{1}{2}\right)(2x) + \left(\dfrac{1}{2}\right)\left(-\dfrac{1}{2}\right)(2x)^2 \dfrac{1}{2} \right.$

$$+ \left(\dfrac{1}{2}\right)\left(-\dfrac{1}{2}\right)\left(-\dfrac{3}{2}\right)(2x)^3 \dfrac{1}{3!}$$

$$\times \left[1 + \left(-\dfrac{1}{2}\right)(-3x) + \left(-\dfrac{1}{2}\right)\left(-\dfrac{3}{2}\right)(-3x)^2 \dfrac{1}{2} \right.$$

$$+ \left(-\dfrac{1}{2}\right)\left(-\dfrac{3}{2}\right)\left(-\dfrac{5}{2}\right)(3x)^3 \dfrac{1}{3!} \Big]$$

The coefficient of x^3

$$\left(-\dfrac{1}{2}\right)\left(-\dfrac{3}{2}\right)\left(-\dfrac{5}{2}\right)(-3)^3 \dfrac{1}{3!} + \left(\dfrac{1}{2}\right)(2)\left(-\dfrac{1}{2}\right)\left(-\dfrac{3}{2}\right)(-3)^2 \dfrac{1}{2}$$

$$+ \left(\dfrac{1}{2}\right)\left(-\dfrac{1}{2}\right)(2)^2 \dfrac{1}{2} \times \left(-\dfrac{1}{2}\right)(-3) + \left(\dfrac{1}{2}\right)\left(-\dfrac{1}{2}\right)\left(-\dfrac{3}{2}\right)(2)^3 \dfrac{1}{3!}$$

$$= \dfrac{135}{16} + \dfrac{27}{8} - \dfrac{3}{4} + \dfrac{1}{2} = \dfrac{185}{16}$$

(ii) $(1 - x)^{-1/2} \, (1 + x)^{-1/2} = [(1 - x)(1 + x)]^{-1/2} = (1 - x^2)^{-1/2}$

$$= 1 + \left(-\frac{1}{2}\right)(-x^2) + \left(-\frac{1}{2}\right)\left(-\frac{3}{2}\right)(x^2)^2 \frac{1}{2}$$

$$= 1 + \frac{1}{2}x^2 + \frac{3}{8}x^4$$

there is no x^3 term, therefore the coefficient of x^3 is zero.

(iii) $\qquad \dfrac{1-x}{(1+x)^3} = (1-x)(1+x)^{-3}$

$$= (-x)\left[1 + (-3)x + (-3)(-4)x^2 \frac{1}{2} + (-3)(-4)(-5)\frac{x^3}{3 \times 2}\right]$$

the coefficient of x^3

$$(-3)(-4)(-5)\frac{1}{2 \times 3} - (-3)(-4)\frac{1}{2} = -10 - 6 = -16$$

7. $\qquad (1-7x)^{-1/3} = 1 + \left(-\frac{1}{3}\right)(-7x) + \left(-\frac{1}{3}\right)\left(-\frac{4}{3}\right)(-7x)^2 \frac{1}{2}$

$$+ \left(-\frac{1}{3}\right)\left(-\frac{4}{3}\right)\left(-\frac{7}{3}\right)(-7x)^3 \frac{1}{3!}$$

$$= 1 + \frac{7}{3}x + \frac{98}{9}x^2 + \frac{4802}{81}x^3.$$

8. $\qquad (a+b)^n = a^n + n\,a^{n-1}b + \dfrac{n(n-1)}{2!}a^{n-2}$

$$+ \ldots + n(n-1)(n-2)\ldots(n-r+1)\,a^{n-r}\frac{b^r}{r!} + \ldots + b^n.$$

The term containing x^r is

$$n(n-1)(n-2)\ldots(n-r+1)\frac{b^r}{r!}$$

9. $\qquad$ The coefficient of x^{25} in the expansion $(1-3x)^{37}$ is

$$^{37}C_{25}(-3)^{25} = \frac{37!}{25!\ 12!}(-3)^{25}.$$

10.

$$g' = \frac{4\pi^2\ l'}{(T')^2} = 4\pi^2\ \frac{\left(l - \dfrac{0.5\ l}{100}\right)}{\left(T + \dfrac{1}{100}T\right)^2} = \frac{4\pi^2\ l}{T^2}\ \frac{(1 - 0.005)}{(1 + 0.01)^2}$$

$$= g\,(1 - 0.0005)\,(1 + 0.01)^{-2}$$

$$= g\,(1 - 0.005)\,\left(1 - 2 \times 0.01 + (-2)\,(-3)\left[0.01)^2\,\frac{1}{2}\right]\right)$$

$$= g\,(1 - 0.005)\,(1 - 0.2 + 0.0003)$$

$$= g\,0.995 \times 0.9803 = g\,0.9753985$$

$$= g\,(1 - 0.0246)$$

The error in g is $- 0.0246$ or $- 2.46\%$.

11. $$f = \frac{K\sqrt{w}}{l} = K\,w^{1/2}\,l^{-1}$$

$$f' = k\,(w')^{1/2}\,(l')^{-1}$$

where $w' = w + 0.01\,w$, $l' = l = 0.02\,l$

$$f' = K\,w^{1/2}\,(1 + 0.01)^{1/2}\,l^{-1}\,(1 - 0.02)^{-1}$$

$$= f\,(1 + 0.01)^{1/2}\,(1 - 0.02)^{-1}\ \times$$

$$= f\left(1 + \frac{0.01}{2} + \left(\frac{1}{2}\right)\left(-\frac{1}{2}\right)(0.01)^2\,\frac{1}{2}\right)$$

$$\left(1 + (-1)\,(-0.02) + (-1)\,(-2)\,\frac{(-0.02)^2}{2}\right)$$

$$= f\left(1 + 0.005 - \frac{0.0001}{8}\right)(1 + 0.02 + 0.0004)$$

$$= 1.025489245f$$

$$= \left(1 + \frac{2.55}{100}\right) f$$

+ 2.25 % the percentage error in the calculated value of f.

12. $\quad (1 + x)^n = 1 + nx + \frac{1}{2} n (n - 1) x^2 + \frac{n (n - 1) (n - 2)}{1 \times 2 \times 3} x^3$

$$= 1 + nx + \frac{1}{2} n (n - 1) x^2 + \frac{n(n - 1) (n - 2)}{6} x^3$$

$$(1 + x)^3 = 1 + 3x + 3 x^2 + x^3$$

If $n = -3$

$$(1 + x)^{-3} = 1 - 3x + 6 x^2 - 10 x^3$$

If $n = - 1/3$

$$(1 + x)^{- 1/3} = 1 - \frac{1}{3} x + \frac{1}{2} \left(- \frac{1}{3}\right) \left(- \frac{4}{3}\right) x^2 + \left(\frac{1}{3}\right) \left(- \frac{4}{3}\right) \left(- \frac{7}{3}\right) \frac{x^3}{1 \times 2 \times 3}$$

$$= 1 - \frac{1}{3} x + \frac{2}{9} x^2 - \frac{14}{81} x^3.$$

13. (i) $\quad \dfrac{1}{(1.005)^{- 3}} = (1 + 0.005)^{-3}$

$$= 1 + (- 3) (0.005) + (- 3) (- 4) (0.005)^2 \frac{1}{2}$$

$$= 1 - 0.015 + 0.000015$$

$$\approx 0.9852$$

(ii) $\quad 27.003^{1/3} = (27 + 0.003)^{1/3} = 3 \left(1 + \frac{0.003}{27}\right)^{1/3}$

$$\approx 3 \left(1 + \frac{1}{3} \frac{0.001}{9} + \frac{1}{3} \left(- \frac{2}{3}\right) \left(\frac{0.001}{9}\right)^2 \frac{1}{2}\right)$$

$$\approx 3 \left(1 + \frac{0.001}{27} \frac{0.000001}{729}\right)$$

$$\approx 3\left(1 + \frac{0.001}{27} - \frac{0.000001}{729}\right)$$

$$\approx 3 + \frac{0.001}{9} = 3.00011$$

(iii) $\quad (1.05)^{1/5} = (1 + 0.05)^{1/5} \approx 1 + \frac{1}{5}0.05 + \frac{1}{5}\left(-\frac{4}{5}\right)(0.05)^2\frac{1}{2}$

$$= 1 + 0.01 - \frac{4}{50}\,0.0025 \approx 1.0098.$$

(iv) $\quad 0.995^{-1/3} = (1 - 0.005)^{-1/3} \approx 1 + \frac{1}{3}\,0.005 - \frac{1}{3}\left(-\frac{2}{3}\right)0.005^2 \times \frac{1}{2}$

$$\approx 1.0017.$$

14. (i) $\quad (1 + x)^{1/2} = 1 + \frac{1}{2}x + \frac{1}{2}\left(-\frac{1}{2}\right)x^2\frac{1}{2} = 1 + \frac{1}{2}x - \frac{1}{8}x^2$

(ii) $\quad (1 - x)^{-3} = 1 + (-3)(-x) + (-3)(-4)(-x)^2\left(\frac{1}{2}\right)$

$$= 1 + 3x + 6x^2$$

$$\frac{(1 + x)^{1/2}}{(1 - x)^3} = (1 + x)^{1/2}(1 - x)^{-3} = \left(1 + \frac{1}{2}x - \frac{1}{8}x^2\right)(1 + 3x + 6x^2)$$

$$= 1 + 3x + 6x^2 + \frac{1}{2}x + \frac{3}{2}x^2 - \frac{1}{8}x^2$$

$$= 1 + \frac{7}{2}x + 7\frac{3}{8}x^2 = 1 + \frac{7}{2}x + \frac{59}{8}x^2.$$

$$\frac{w^{1/2}\left(1 + \frac{1}{100}\right)^{1/2}}{z^3\left(1 - \frac{1}{100}\right)^3} = \frac{w^{1/2}}{z^3}\left(1 + \frac{1}{100}\right)^{1/2}\left(1 - \frac{1}{100}\right)^{-3}$$

$$= \frac{w^{1/2}}{z^3}\left(1 + \frac{7}{2}\frac{1}{100} + \frac{59}{8}\frac{1}{100^2}\right) = \frac{w^{1/2}}{z^3}(1 + 0.03574).$$

The percentage change in $w^{1/2}/z^3$ is $+ 3.57\%$

15.
$$(1 + bx)^{-n} = 1 + (- n) (bx) + (- n) (- n - 1) (bx)^2 \frac{1}{2} +$$

$$(- n) (- n - 1) (- n - 2) (bx)^3 \frac{1}{3!}$$

$$= 1 - nbx + n (n + 1) \frac{b^2 x^2}{2} - n (n + 1) (n + 2) \frac{b^3 x^3}{3!}$$

$$1 + 5x + 9 x^2 + a x^3.$$

Equating coefficients we have:

for x, $- nb = 5 \ldots(1)$

for x^2, $\quad \dfrac{n (n + 1) b^2}{2} = 9 \ldots(2)$

for $x^3 \quad \dfrac{-n (n + 1) (n + 2)}{6} b^3 = a \ldots(3)$

From (1), $b = -\dfrac{5}{n}$ and substituting this value in (2), $n (n + 1)\left(-\dfrac{5}{n}\right)^2 =$

$$\frac{(n + 1)}{n} = \frac{18}{25}$$

$$1 + \frac{1}{n} = \frac{18}{25}$$

$$\boxed{n = -\frac{25}{7}}$$

$$b = -\frac{5}{n} = \frac{-5}{-25/7} = \frac{7}{5}$$

$$\boxed{b = \frac{7}{5}}$$

$$a = \frac{(-n)(n+1)(n+2)b^3}{6} = \frac{\left(\frac{25}{7}\right)\left(-\frac{18}{7}\right)\left(-\frac{11}{7}\right)\left(\frac{7}{5}\right)^3}{6}$$

$$= \frac{25 \times 18 \times 11 \times 7^3}{7^3 \times 125 \times 6} = \frac{33}{5}$$

16.
$$\left(x - \frac{1}{x^2}\right)^5 \left(x + \frac{1}{x}\right)^9 = x^5\left(1 - \frac{1}{x^3}\right)^5 x^9\left(1 + \frac{1}{x^2}\right)^9 = x^{14}\left(1 - \frac{1}{x^3}\right)^5\left(1 + \frac{1}{x^2}\right)^9$$

$$= x^{14}\left(1 - \frac{5}{x^3} + \frac{10}{x^6} - \frac{10}{x^9} + \cdots\right)\left(1 + \frac{9}{x^2} + \frac{36}{x^4} + \frac{84}{x^6} + \frac{126}{x^8} + \frac{126}{x^{10}} + \frac{84}{x^{12}} + \frac{36}{x^{14}} + \cdots\right)$$

The term independent of x is $x^{14}\dfrac{36}{x^{14}} = 36.$

SOLUTION 8

1.
$$e^x = 1 + \frac{x}{1!} + \frac{x^2}{2!} + \frac{x^3}{3!} + \frac{x^4}{4!}$$

2.
$$e^{-x} = 1 - \frac{x}{1!} + \frac{x^2}{2!} - \frac{x^3}{3!} + \frac{x^4}{4!}$$

3.
$$e^{-1} = 1 - \frac{1}{1!} + \frac{1^2}{2!} - \frac{1^3}{3!} + \frac{1^4}{4!} = 1 - 1 + \frac{1}{2} - \frac{1}{6} + \frac{1}{24} = 0.7083$$

4. (i)
$$e = 1 + \frac{1}{1!} + \frac{1}{2!} + \frac{1}{3!} + \frac{1}{4!}$$

(ii)
$$e^{-1} = \frac{1}{e} = 1 - 1 + \frac{1}{2} - \frac{1}{6} + \frac{1}{24}$$

(iii)
$$\frac{1}{e^2} = e^{-2} = 1 - \frac{2}{1!} + \frac{2^2}{2!} - \frac{2^3}{3!} + \frac{2^4}{4!}$$

(iv)
$$\frac{1}{2}\left(e + \frac{1}{e}\right) = \frac{1}{2}\left(1 + 1 + \frac{1}{2} + \frac{1}{6} + \frac{1}{24} + 1 - 1 + \frac{1}{2} - \frac{1}{6} + \frac{1}{24}\right)$$

$$= \frac{1}{2}\left(2 + \frac{1}{2} + \frac{1}{12}\right) = \frac{1}{2}\left(\frac{5}{2} + \frac{1}{12}\right) = \frac{5}{4} + \frac{1}{24} = \frac{31}{24}$$

(v)
$$\frac{1}{2}\left(e - \frac{1}{e}\right) = \frac{1}{2}\left(1 + 1 + \frac{1}{2} + \frac{1}{6} + \frac{1}{24} - 1 + 1 - \frac{1}{2} + \frac{1}{6} - \frac{1}{24}\right)$$

$$= \frac{1}{2}\left(2 + \frac{1}{3}\right) = 1 + \frac{1}{6} = \frac{7}{6}.$$

5. (i) $2\,e^{3x} = 2\left(1 + 3\dfrac{x}{1!} \; x \; \dfrac{(3x)^2}{2!} + \dfrac{(3x)^3}{3!} + \dfrac{(3x)^4}{4!} + \dfrac{(3x)^5}{5!}\right)$

$$= 2\left(1 + 3x + \dfrac{9}{2}\,x^2 + \dfrac{9}{2}\,x^3 + \dfrac{27}{8}\,x^4 + \dfrac{81}{40}\,x^5\right)$$

$$= 2 + 6x + 9\,x^2 + 9\,x^3 + \dfrac{27}{4}\,x^4 + \dfrac{81}{20}\,x^5$$

(ii) $3\,e^{-2x} = 3\left(1 + \dfrac{(-2x)}{1!} + \dfrac{(-2x)^2}{2!} + \dfrac{(-2x)^3}{3!} + \dfrac{(-2x)^4}{4!} + \dfrac{(-2x)^5}{5!}\right)$

$$= 3\left(1 - 2x + 2\,x^2 - \dfrac{4}{3}x^3 + \dfrac{2}{3}\,x^4 - \dfrac{4}{15}\,x^5\right)$$

$$= 3 - 6x + 6\,x^2 - 4\,x^3 + 2\,x^4 - \dfrac{4}{5}\,x^5$$

(iii) $5\,e^{-x} = 5\left(1 - x + \dfrac{x^2}{2} - \dfrac{x^3}{6} + \dfrac{x^4}{24} - \dfrac{x^5}{120}\right)$

$$= 5 - 5x + \dfrac{5}{2}\,x^2 - \dfrac{5}{6}\,x^3 + \dfrac{5}{24}\,x^4 - \dfrac{1}{24}\,x^5$$

(iv) $4\left(1 + \dfrac{(x/2)}{1!} + \dfrac{(x/2)^2}{2!} + \dfrac{(x/2)^3}{3!} + \dfrac{(x/2)^4}{4!} + \dfrac{(x/2)^5}{5!}\right)$

$$= 4\left(1 + \dfrac{1}{2}\,x + \dfrac{1}{8}\,x^2 + \dfrac{1}{48}\,x^3 + \dfrac{1}{384}\,x^4 + \dfrac{1}{3840}\,x^5\right)$$

$$= 4 + 2\,x + \dfrac{1}{2}\,x^2 + \dfrac{1}{12}\,x^3 + \dfrac{1}{96}\,x^4 + \dfrac{1}{960}\,x^5$$

(v) $e^{-3/2x} = 1 - \dfrac{3}{2}\dfrac{x}{1!} + \dfrac{9}{4}\dfrac{x^2}{2!} - \dfrac{27}{8}\dfrac{x^3}{31} + \dfrac{81}{16}\dfrac{x^4}{4!} - \dfrac{243x^5}{32}$

$$= 1 - \dfrac{3}{2}\,x + \dfrac{9}{8}\,x^2 - \dfrac{9}{16}\,x^3 + \dfrac{27}{128}\,x^4 - \dfrac{81}{1280}\,x^5$$

6. (i) $e^{0.55} = 1 + \dfrac{0.55}{1} + \dfrac{0.55^2}{2} + \dfrac{0.55^3}{6} + \dfrac{0.55^4}{24} + \dfrac{0.55^5}{120} + \dfrac{0.55^6}{720} + \dfrac{0.55^7}{5040}$

$= 1 + 0.55 + 0.15125 + 0.0277291 + 0.0038127604 + 0.00041940365$

$+ 0.000038445334 + 0.0000030207048$

$= 1.7332527$

$= 1.733$ to four significant figures from the calculator $e^{0.55}$
$= 1.733253 = 1.733$ to four significant figures.

(ii) $e^{-3.5} = 1 - 3.5 + \dfrac{3.5^2}{2} - \dfrac{3.5^3}{6} + \dfrac{3.5^4}{24} - \dfrac{3.5^5}{120} - \dfrac{3.5^7}{5040} + \dfrac{3.5^8}{8!}$

$= 1 - 3.5 + 6.125 - 7.1458333 + 6.2526042 - 4.3768229$
$\quad + 2.5531467 - 1.2765734 + 0.5585008$
$= 0.1850224 = 0.185$ to four significant figures, note that
we have taken nine terms instead of eight terms since the answer for eight

terms is negative and equal to -0.3734784 but $e^{-3.5} = \dfrac{1}{e^{3.5}}$ is greater
than zero.

(iii) $e^{0.02} = 1 + \dfrac{0.02}{1} + \dfrac{0.02^2}{2!} + \dfrac{0.02^3}{6} + \dfrac{0.02^4}{24} + \dfrac{0.02^5}{120} + \dfrac{0.02^6}{720} + \dfrac{0.02^7}{5040}$

$= 1 + 0.02 + 0.0002 + 1.3333 \times 10^{-6} + 6.6666 \times 10^{-9} + \text{small}$

$= 1.0202013 = 1.020$ to four significant figures

From the calculator $e^{0.02} = 1.0202013$.

7.   Find the first three terms of the series

$\dfrac{e^x - e^{-x}}{e^x} = \dfrac{e^x}{e^x} - \dfrac{e^{-x}}{e^x} = 1 - e^{2x}$

$e^{-2x} = 1 - 2x + \dfrac{(2x)^2}{2} - \dfrac{(2x)^3}{6} = 1 - 2x + 2x^2 - \dfrac{4}{3}x^3.$

Therefore the first three terms of the series

$1 - e^{-2x} = 1 - \left(1 - 2x + 2x^2 - \dfrac{4}{3}x^3\right)$

8.	In the expansion of e^x these are infinite number of terms.

	The terms converge, that is, they become smaller and smaller.

9.	The special property of the exponential function e^x is that the gradient of any point is the same as the function.

$$y = e^x \text{ and } \frac{dy}{dx} = e^x.$$

10.	If x increases, then $y = e^x$ increases abruptly.

If	$x = 1, y = 2.718$
	$x = 2, y = 7.389$
	$x = 3, y = 20.086$
	$x = 4, y = 54.598\#$

SOLUTION 9

1.	(i)	$180°$ are equivalent to π radians, $x°$ are equivalent $\dfrac{x\pi}{180}$

	radians.

$$5° \equiv \left(\frac{5\pi}{180}\right)^c = 0.0872664^c$$

(ii)	$2° \equiv \left(\dfrac{2\pi}{180}\right) = 0.0349065^c$

(iii)	$15' \equiv \left(\dfrac{15}{60}\right)\dfrac{\pi}{180}$ radians $= 4.3633231 \times 10^{-3}$ radians

(iv)	$5' = 4.3633231 \times 10^{-3} = 1.454441 \times 10^{-3}$ radians

(v)	$2' = \dfrac{2}{5} 1.454441 \times 10^{-3} = 5.817764 \times 10^{-4}$ radians

2.	(i)	π radians are equivalent to $180°$ x radians are equivalent $\dfrac{180x}{\pi}$ degrees

$$0.05^c = \frac{180}{\pi} 0.05 = 2.87°$$

(ii) $\quad 0.5^c = \dfrac{180}{\pi}\, 0.5 = 28.7°$

(iii) $\quad 0.00015^c = \dfrac{180}{\pi}\, 0.000115 = 8.5943669 x\ 10^{-3}$ degrees

$$= 0.515662 \text{ minutes}$$
$$= 31 \text{ seconds}$$

(iv) $\quad 1^c = \dfrac{180}{\pi} \times 1 = 57.3°.$

3. (i) $\quad \sin 1.5' = \sin \left(\dfrac{1.5}{60}\ \dfrac{\pi}{180}\right)^c \approx \dfrac{1.5}{60}\ \dfrac{\pi}{180} = 4.36 \times 10^{-4}$
(ii) $\quad \sin 0.05^c \approx 0.05$

(iii) $\quad \sin 0.75° = \sin \left(\dfrac{0.75\pi}{180}\right)^c \approx \dfrac{0.75\pi}{180} = 0.0131$

(iv) $\quad \tan 0.5° = \tan \left(\dfrac{0.5\pi}{180}\right)^c \approx \dfrac{0.5\pi}{180} = 8.73 x\ 10^{-3}$

(v) $\quad \cos 1' = \cos \left(\dfrac{1}{60}^\circ\right) \cos \left(\dfrac{1}{60}\ \dfrac{\pi}{180}\right) \approx 1 - \left(\dfrac{\pi}{60} \times 180\right)^2 \dfrac{1}{2} = 0.9999999$

(vi) $\quad \cos 0.75° = \cos \left(\dfrac{0.75\pi}{180}\right) \approx 1 - \left(\dfrac{0.75\pi}{180}\right)^2 \dfrac{1}{2}$

$$\cos 0.75° = 0.9999143$$

(vii) $\quad \cos 25' - \cos \left(\dfrac{25}{60}\right)° = \cos \left(\dfrac{25}{60}\ \dfrac{\pi}{180}\right) \approx 1 - \left(\dfrac{25}{60}\ \dfrac{\pi}{180}\right)^2 \dfrac{1}{2}$

$$\cos 25' = 0.9999735$$

4. $\quad y = 30 \sin 31420t$

(i) the amplitude is 30

(ii) the frequency is found from $2\pi f = 31420$

therefore $f = \dfrac{31420}{2\pi} = 500 \text{ Hz}$

(iii)   the period $T = \dfrac{1}{f} = \dfrac{1}{5000} = 0.2\ \text{ms}$

(iv) ω = angular velocity = 31420 radians/sec

5. $\omega t = \theta$
     $t = \theta / \omega$.

Θ°	0	30	60	90	120	150
Θ^{c}	0	$\pi/6$	$\pi/3$	$\pi/2$	$2\pi/3$	$5\pi/6$
		$\pi/6\,\omega$	$\pi/3\,\omega$			
t	0	$\pi/6\,\omega$	$\pi/3\,\omega$	$\pi/2\,\omega$	$2\pi/3\,\omega$	$5\pi/6\,\omega$

180	210	240	270	300	330	360
π	$7\pi/6$	$4\pi/3$	$3\pi/2$	$5\pi/3$	$11\pi/6$	2π
π/ω	$7\pi/6\,\omega$	$4\pi/3\,\omega$	$3\pi/2\,\omega$	$5\pi/3\,\omega$	$11\pi/6\,\omega$	$2\pi/\omega$

6.

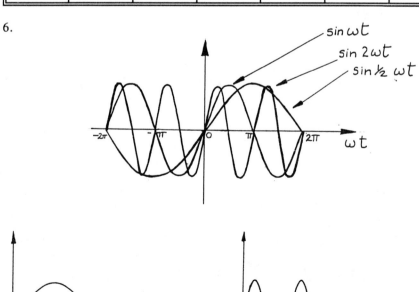

7.

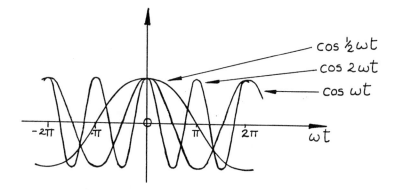

cos ½ωt
cos 2ωt
cos ωt

8.   Similar to the above (6)

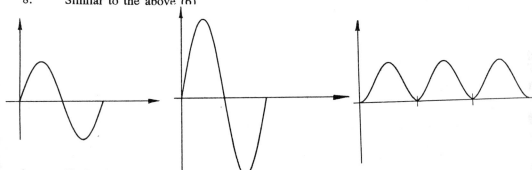

9.   Similar to the above (1)

10.

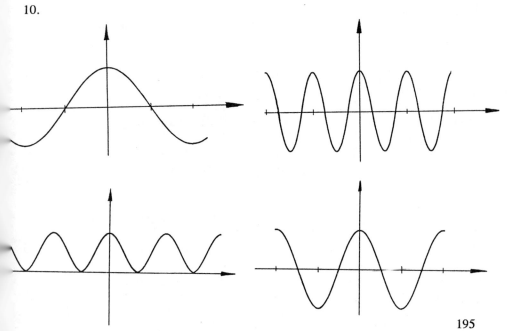

INDEX